INVESTIGATI\
INTERVIEWIN
EXPLAINED

This book is based upon experience of investigative interviewing - not simply the experience of the authors but also the experience of the many investigators they have had the privilege of working with over several decades

INVESTIGATIVE INTERVIEWING explained

*The operational guide to
practical interviewing skills*

Brian Ord
Gary Shaw

Investigative Interviewing Explained

© Brian Ord & Gary Shaw

First edition 1999
The New Police Bookshop

ISBN: 0 9533058 2 1

The New Police Bookshop
Surrey, England, UK
(Benson Publications)
PO Box 124, Woking
GU22 9XT

The New Police Bookshop
East Yorkshire, England, UK
(Law Authentication Work)
PO Box 124, Goole
DN14 7FH

Cover reproduction by Chalvington Press
Petworth, West Sussex
Printed and bound by The Cromwell Press
Trowbridge, Wiltshire
Distributed by Brookland Mailing Services, Bristol

To order
Tel 0117 9555 215 Fax 0117 9541 485
Email npb@brookservices.demon.co.uk

Contents

PART ONE: CORE SKILLS

PART TWO: STRUCTURING INTERVIEWS

PART THREE: THE LAW

Forewords

In recent times, the emphasis of modern policing has been to prevent crimes before they occur. Significant success has been achieved by police and their partners in this aim, with crime figures falling nationally. One of the techniques that has been particularly successful is our intelligence led approach which focuses on the criminal. Interviewing skills have never been more crucial in this worthy enterprise.

Such skills have to be displayed by officers thousands of times each day the length and breadth of the country, as they carry out their investigations. Indeed, interviewing people, whether they are suspects, victims or witnesses, is a crucial and integral part of policing.

The importance of investigative interviewing has been recognised over recent years as being vital to the effective investigation of crime. This book provides the reader with an easy-to-read and easy-to-understand guide to investigative interviewing. It is a practical and comprehensive guide with helpful examples which will assist officers in developing and honing their investigative skills. I commend it to you.

John Stevens
Deputy Commissioner Metropolitan Police
(Formerly Chief Constable of Northumbria)

November 1998

Investigating crime has never been more demanding. With the Police and Criminal Evidence Act of 1984 and its Codes of Practice, the tape recording of interview - and the forensic examination in court of every activity by the police, from the commission of the crime to the trial - professionalism is absolutely essential. A critical part of any investigation is the interview, both with witnesses and with the suspect, whether under arrest or not.

I have spent 35 years as a police officer - many as an investigator - and as a former graduate of the the FBI Academy in Quantico, I know only too well the pitfalls and problems involved in learning the craft of interviewing. This practical guide to investigative interviewing provides an easy-to-read, hands-on journey through the whole process. Having been a member of the Home Office working group on investigative interviewing which developed the current practice, I fully understand the importance and difficulties of the training of such a complex subject. The two authors bring to this book decades of experience in crime investigation and the text is set out in an eminently readable format. I regret that such a guide was not available in my early years as a detective and I have little doubt that the sensible advice it contains will endure.

In my professional judgement this work is required reading for all police officers, or any other person tasked with the responsibility of investigation. A legal minefield has been made safer. I wish the book well.

Brian Mackenzie
House of Lords
London

November 1998

The authors

Brian Ord and Gary Shaw have 50 years' experience between them with Northumbria Police and the vast majority of this has been devoted to crime investigation.

They have dealt with every category of crime, and have substantial experience of dealing with murder, armed robbery, terrorism, and a wide variety of serious sexual offences. During 1991 they were jointly involved in a long-term investigation that rid the North East of England of professional ram-raider gangs.

Brian Ord was one of the pioneers of tape recording police interviews with suspects and the development of police officers' skills in investigative interviewing. He rose to the rank of detective superintendent and retired from the police service in 1994. He continues his involvement in training courses in investigative interviewing and the investigation of offences for commercial organisations.

Gary Shaw is a former member of the national investigative interviewing project team at Bramshill and continues to be actively involved in this field, contributing to seminars and training courses. He is now detective inspector in a major crime investigation unit.

Their motivation in producing this book arises from their recognition of a need for a practical guide in investigative interviewing for all police officers, whether patrol constables, detectives or senior officers managing the investigation of serious crime.

PART ONE

CORE SKILLS

1. Preparation and planning

2. Establishing rapport

3. Questioning

4. Listening

CHAPTER 1

PREPARATION AND PLANNING

Introduction

Preparation and planning before an interview is vitally important, yet it is rarely given the time and the attention it deserves. The most common excuses used by interviewers are lack of time, and pressures from supervisors or custody officers to proceed with interviews before they are ready to do so.

There is no doubt such pressures do exist, as the police are legally bound to conduct investigations promptly, particularly once a person is in custody.

Police managers and custody officers have a responsibility to ensure prisoners are dealt with diligently and speedily, but they have an equally important function of ensuring that offences are properly investigated. Diligent investigation can only be carried out by investigators who are adequately prepared to conduct the investigation and they must be allowed reasonable time to prepare and plan the interview.

Investigating officers must bear in mind that they share the responsibility for dealing with detained persons expediently, and failure to do so may have an adverse effect on the outcome of the case. There is little point in conducting an interview if it is later excluded by the courts due to some legal technicality arising from a breach of the Police and Criminal Evidence Act or other legislation.

On some occasions it will be possible to delay arrests and interviews until adequate preparation and planning has been completed, but on many occasions events will be more spontaneous and require early interviews. In any event there is always some time available for preparation and planning, and whatever time is available should be used productively.

> *Investigating officers should whenever possible follow the dictum 'investigate then interview' rather than 'interview then investigate'.*

The disadvantages of poor preparation and planning

There are obvious disadvantages to starting an interview prematurely without adequate preparation and planning.

Fig 1

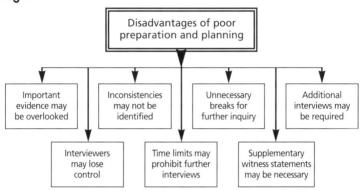

Overlooking evidence - While the interview is in progress, interviewers must assimilate what is being said, bearing in mind what is already known or believed. Those who do not have a good grasp of the investigation are unlikely to recognise some evidential facts as they emerge. Important evidence that could have been gained from questions put to a suspect may be lost. When interviewing either witnesses or suspects, if you do not ask the question you are unlikely to receive the answer.

Failing to identify inconsistencies and lies - Interviewers who lack knowledge of the wider aspects of the matter under investigation are unlikely to identify things said which are either inconsistent with known facts or deliberate lies.

Unnecessary breaks in the interviews - Interviewers who start interviewing prematurely are more likely to be forced to stop the interview part way through to make further inquiries. This is waste of valuable investigative time.

Unnecessary additional interviews - Further time-consuming interviews may be necessary with witnesses and suspects to explore matters which have emerged during the interview, but which were readily identifiable beforehand had the interviewer prepared adequately.

Loss of control of the interview - Ill-prepared interviewers may have difficulty controlling the direction of an interview and can soon lose credibility in the eyes of the interviewee. Suspects may quickly capitalise on lack of knowledge and take control. A witness may interpret lack of knowledge as lack of interest and conclude there is little point in providing information to someone who appears uninterested and unlikely to act upon any information given.

Time constraints - Facts emerging after a person has been charged may not, in certain circumstances, be legally put to the suspect and this could result in loss of crucial evidence.

Additional witness statements may be necessary - Supplementary witness statements may be necessary from witnesses to cover facts that were missed during the interview. Witnesses later challenged upon this in court may have difficulty in justifying their apparent failure to mention evidence at the time of the first interview.

The essentials of preparation and planning

The terms 'preparation' and 'planning' should not be considered individually but as a collective process consisting of four component parts.

Fig 2

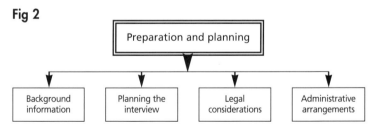

Background information

A good knowledge of the circumstances surrounding the offence under investigation - and of the character and background of the person to be interviewed - is vital if the interviewer is to succeed in his task. This is so whether it is a witness, victim or a suspect who is to be interviewed.

Background to the incident under investigation

The more that interviewers know about the incident under investigation, the more competent they will be in conducting the investigation, and the more able they will be to adapt to changing circumstances during the interview.

Fig 3

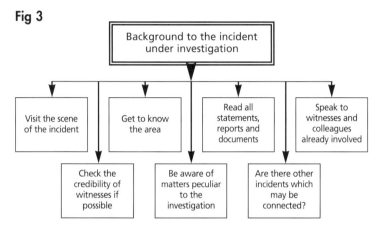

Interviewers should consider all particulars leading up to the incident in detail, including:

Visit the scene - Interviewers should visit the scene of the incident and carefully observe the area. Note anything that may have been left at the scene, or anything that may have been removed from it. Photographs taken of a scene may be helpful in some cases.

Know the geographical area - Make yourself aware of the general geographical area. You may need to refer to streets or buildings and it is helpful if you can picture the situation being described. There may be merit in returning to the scene with witnesses, or even suspects in some circumstances.

Read available documents - Read any statements, incident reports or any other documentation relating to the offence.

Speak to witnesses - If possible, speak personally to any witnesses or other persons connected to the incident, including colleagues who have attended the scene or spoken to material witnesses.

Check upon credibility of witnesses - Check on the credibility of the person providing evidence against a suspect, including the victim or any witnesses. Even a person of bad character can provide reliable evidence on occasions but the interviewer should be aware of a dubious reputation.

Knowledge of matters peculiar to the investigation - The interviewer must familiarise himself with any matters peculiar to the investigation. For example, in a fraud investigation, knowledge of the system of bookkeeping and accounting is essential to the investigator, whether he is interviewing the accounts clerk or a fraudster.

Knowledge of similar incidents - The matter being investigated may be part of a series, or connected with other incidents which may have been reported in the same area. For example a report of a house burglary in a street may be connected with a suspicious incident reported earlier.

Background character of the person to be interviewed
Get to know the witness' or suspect's background as this can help your understanding and assessment of information they provide. Always keep an open mind - robbers can be robbed and prostitutes can be raped.

Fig 4

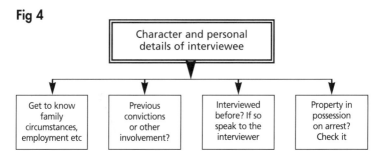

The following personal data may be of interest:

Family circumstances - Marital status, family, employment and other personal details should be ascertained.

Past history of interviewee - Check whether or not the witness or suspect has a criminal record or is the subject of crime intelligence. Have they previously been involved in, or reported, an incident?

Former involvement - Have other officers interviewed or dealt with them in the past? If so speak to them and ascertain their views.

Prisoner's property - When the person to be interviewed has been arrested, the property in his possession on arrest should be carefully examined. It may provide evidence relating to the matter under investigation, other offences, or negate an alibi.

Once the background to the offence has been examined and the personal details of the interviewee have been checked, interviewers should ask themselves if there any other inquiries which should be made before the interview starts.

Time well spent at this stage can help in the long term,
increasing the likelihood of a successful interview.

Planning the interview

Officers must fully understand the reason for the interview and be able to distinguish between the 'purpose' and the 'aim' of the interview and the 'objectives'.

The purpose of the interview - The purpose of an investigative interview will remain the same throughout. Whether it is a witness, a victim or a suspect who is being interviewed, the purpose of the interview is to ascertain the truth of the matter under investigation.

The aim of the interview - The aim is usually more specific, although the scope must be broad enough to take in any unexpected developments. The aim may vary depending on the circumstances of each case and whether the interview is with a witness or a suspect. For example, with a suspect, the aim may be to establish whether or not they were involved in the offence - NOT to prove their involvement in the offence. It is as important for an interviewer to establish who was not involved in a crime, as to find out who was. With a witness, the aim may be to ascertain their knowledge, if any, of the matter being investigated.

The objectives - Once the aim of the interview has been established the interviewer can formulate the objectives - the steps toward achieving the aim.

Fig 5

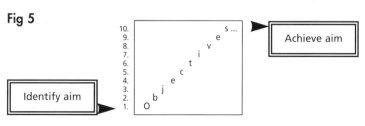

Fig 6

Example

The suspect interview
Aim - to establish if the suspect was involved in the burglary.
Objectives -
1. To find out what he says he was doing at the material time
2. How can he support this? - for example who was he with?
3. If elsewhere - what was he doing?
4. What/who did he see?
5. What else did he see?

The witness interview
For a witness who has seen the suspect commit the burglary, the aim and the objectives could be as follows:
Aim - to establish if the witness can identify the suspect.
Objectives -
1. How long was the suspect in view?
2. What distance was the witness from him?
3. What was the visibility at the time?
4. Is the suspect known to the witness - if so, how long has he known him?
5. Are there any special reasons for remembering the suspect?
6. Are there any differences between the description provided and the suspect's actual appearance?

The aim is the long-term destination, whereas the objectives are the short term means of achieving the aim.

The aim of the interview should be noted on the written interview plan as a reminder of the intended direction of the interview, and this should be followed by a list of the objectives.

The objectives can be divided into three main areas concerning:
- what is already known;
- what needs to be determined;
- the points that need to be proved.

The interviewer should conduct a detailed analysis of what is already known, the points which need to be proved and what else is required. In a case in which a defence may be put forward, a further objective may be to identify whether the defence is applicable or not. A degree of caution should be exercised by the interviewer so as not to to encourage the dishonest suspect to falsely adjust his account and thus avail himself of a possible defence. A tactful approach should afford the suspect every opportunity to provide his account without putting words into his mouth.

All available material will need to be examined to formulate the interview plan. This will include written statements, incident or crime reports, notes made at the scene, and notes made from the verbal accounts of others who have yet to make statements. This should identify the possible offences and from this the points to be proved and defences can be determined.

The easiest way to manage this information is to write down all relevant matters. Once this is done, the items can be grouped together in a logical sequence in the form of objectives and recorded formally on the written interview plan. The notes should consist of key words - single words where possible - printed in large letters to provide recall cues which can be taken in at a glance.

An interview plan should be used for all interviews, whether with suspects, witnesses or victims, and is particularly important when dealing with suspects. It allows the interviewer to steer the interview in the appropriate direction and to keep track of all matters which should be covered. A well-prepared interview plan can be quickly adjusted in the event of unexpected events arising during the course of the interview.

Legal considerations

There is little point in conducting well-prepared and detailed interviews only to find at a later stage that the interview is inadmissible as evidence because of a breach of the terms of the Police and Criminal Evidence Act, the Codes of Practice or any other legislation.

Interviewers require a sound knowledge of the law and need to be particularly mindful of aspects that could result in courts excluding evidence because of a breach in the law. Prior to interview, interviewers should ask themselves the following questions:

All interviews
Is the person to be interviewed:
- a juvenile?
- mentally handicapped or mentally disordered?

If so, have arrangements been made for an appropriate adult to attend?

Does the witness or suspect appear to be:
- blind, or seriously visually handicapped?
- deaf?
- unable to read?
- unable to speak, or have speech difficulties?
- unable to understand English?

If so, ensure an interpreter is readily available.

Interviews with suspects
- Is the legal representative available?
- In the case of a detained person, is he approaching a period of rest - if so should the interview be delayed?
- Is a special warning appropriate?
- Has the suspect made a significant statement (or silence) that needs to be dealt with?
- What evidence is to be disclosed before and during the interview to the suspect and/or his legal representative?

All of those points are better addressed well in advance of the interview - a great deal of time will be saved in the long term.

Administrative arrangements

Once all the relevant background information has been gathered, the interview plan has been formulated and legal aspects have been addressed, the final stage is to deal with any administrative matters which will help the interview to progress smoothly.

If a suspect is to be interviewed, the interview will normally take place at a police station. The interviewer should check that the interview room is available, that the tape recording machine is functioning, that there are sufficient seats for the number of persons to be present at the interview, and that the room is in a condition which reflects the professionalism of the event about to take place. Make sure there are sufficient cassette tapes, sealing labels, and any other forms that may be required during the interview. Make sure that exhibits, sketch plans, statements, or records of interview which may need to be referred to are available. Remember that any notes of previous conversations with the suspect may need to be signed or referred to, and check that these are available.

Some of these matters will also apply in a victim or witness interview at a police station but, when an interview has to be conducted somewhere other than police premises, check the facilities available and take all relevant documentation with you.

The interviewer must ensure that any other persons who need to be present are available and are fully aware of the time and place of the interview and, where necessary, have been fully briefed as to their requirements.

Summary

Most interviewers have experienced occasions when unexpected facts emerge during the course of the interview and the whole complexion of the investigation has changed instantly. The interviewer may be left with the choice of either postponing the interview or ploughing on regardless although at a severe disadvantage. Often in the case of suspect interviews, time will not allow postponement and important evidence can be lost.

An essential ingredient for good interviews is flexibility, and interviewers should be prepared to adapt to a changing situation. Good preparation will allow for this and minimise the risk of control of the interview being lost.

The advantages of good preparation and planning:

√ Provides a sound basis for the interview.
√ Enables both important evidential facts on the one hand, and inconsistencies on the other, to be identified more readily.
√ Allows the well-prepared interviewer to review his interview plan quickly should unexpected events arise, and to maintain control of the interview.
√ Saves time in the long term as good preparation can eliminate the need for additional interviews.
√ Inspires the person being interviewed with confidence and respect in the interviewer, as he appears professional and credible.
√ Allows the well-prepared interviewer to exercise flexibility, and to steer the interview in accordance with the interview plan.

It will not always be practicable for the interviewer to prepare and plan to the degree described because the time available will vary depending upon individual circumstances. Nevertheless it is up to interviewers to use the time they do have wisely, and to the best effect.

To be a successful interviewer one has to be well prepared, and those who constantly strive to achieve high standards will achieve high credibility, commanding respect not only from those whom they interview, but also colleagues and other professionals associated with the criminal justice system.

CHAPTER 2

ESTABLISHING RAPPORT

Introduction

Establishing rapport means 'getting into communication with'. In social conversations where the participants are well known to each other, rapport is either already in existence or can be quickly established. As a result, uninhibited communication flows from an early stage of the conversation.

Police interviews can present a very different situation. Frequently the participants are meeting for the first time, and the relationship between interviewers and those being interviewed can be artificial. Suspects, witnesses and victims may be unaccustomed to dealing with the police and, due to the strange surroundings and the new experience, they may feel tense, nervous and insecure. It is unlikely in such situations that conversation will flow readily. A warming-up period is required, and the earlier some kind of rapport can be established, the earlier information will begin to pass between the parties involved.

It is the responsibility of police interviewers to help create a working relationship at the earliest possible stage of their involvement with persons who are to be interviewed.

Rapport is not a friendship, nor is it a kinship of like minds. It is the development of a trusting relationship between the interviewer and interviewee and should be maintained throughout the whole of the interview. It matters not whether the interviewee is a witness, victim or suspect, the purpose of the interview is the same, to obtain information. Interviewees will be more inclined to impart information if they feel comfortable in the company of the interviewer.

Police officers can gain a greater appreciation of how an interviewee feels by reflecting back upon their own experience of being interviewed. Few people relish the prospect of being interviewed, whether it be a job interview, promotion board, live media interview or any other kind. The interviewer who understands this anxiety is more likely to manage the conversation properly and achieve the required objectives.

The key to establishing rapport

Fig 7

Your own experience?

Think back to a past job interview or promotion board you have personally experienced. How did the interviewer handle it? Were you kept waiting nervously in a waiting area and eventually presented to the interviewers by someone not involved in the actual interview? After a brief introduction, did the interviewers begin firing questions on a wide range of topics?

Did you feel you were just getting into the swing of things and beginning to communicate freely when the interview was abruptly terminated?

Would you have reacted differently if the interviewer had met you in the waiting area, courteously explained the procedures about to take place, and described the topics to be covered? Would it have helped if the interviewer had asked you before entering the interview room if you had any questions or concerns, and then escorted you personally to the interview room?

Had you been dealt with in this way would the interview have started in earnest much earlier? Would the interviewers have gained more information about you and your knowledge of the topics covered? Would this have assisted them in making a more informed decision about you, and what you had to say?

If the interviewers had given you individual treatment and shown that they genuinely cared about you and your views, would it have helped reduce the anxiety you felt, and would they have been more likely to achieve their objectives?

   The key to establishing rapport with suspects, witnesses and victims can be divided into six main areas:

- I   creating a good impression from the outset;
- I   treating the interviewee as an individual;
- I   understanding the feelings of the person being interviewed;
- I   explaining the reason for the interview;
- I   giving an outline of the procedures and the reasons for them;
- I   describing the format of the interview.

Fig 8

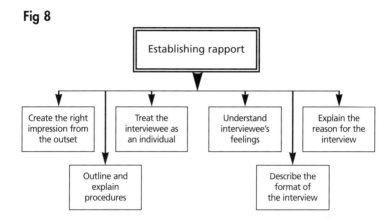

First impressions

The police officer should aim for a friendly and courteous approach to a potential interviewee whenever possible, and from the outset the officer should aim to appear professional and knowledgeable. This will help the early development of a trustworthy relationship in which the interviewee will feel comfortable to impart information to the interviewer.

A witness, victim or suspect who, when meeting the police officer, forms the impression that he is approachable, interested and professional, is much more likely to communicate freely during the interview than if a contrary view is formed. Interviewers have a greater prospect of achieving their objectives if they create the right impression on initial contact.

Even in the face of adversity with hostile suspects, reluctant witnesses or unco-operative victims, there is a greater prospect of eventual co-operation when officers portray a professional image, taking care not to allow their own emotions to take over. Some offenders may use abuse and anger in a deliberate attempt to gain a similar reaction from the police officer. The officer who succumbs to this has allowed the offender to achieve his objective of preventing the interview taking place.

> *Interviewers should be conscious of the old adage - you catch more flies with sugar than you do with vinegar. Courtesy, politeness and understanding cost nothing but can greatly contribute to a successful interview.*

Treat the interviewee as an individual

Police officers who treat interviewees individually, and with consideration and respect, are much more likely to achieve their objectives by creating the right atmosphere in which a successful interview can be conducted. It is a normal human reaction to respond favourably to individual treatment, and interviewees who identify that they are receiving this are more likely to feel at ease in the company of the interviewer. This then inspires confidence and respect in the interviewer and increases the possibility of a free flow of information in which vital evidence may be revealed.

We all have a preference for the way we like to be addressed, and the interviewer who takes the time to ascertain this from the outset is likely to gain respect. Most people have experienced situations when they have been addressed by the wrong name, and some of us may have been guilty of doing this to others. It does nothing to enhance the interviewer's credibility. Interviewees can be forgiven for feeling there is little point in communicating with a person who has not taken the time to find out their name, and also for believing it is an indication of the interviewer's attitude to the investigation as a whole. The more an interviewer knows about the interviewees the better, and he should at least be aware of how they prefer to be addressed.

Individual interviewees have their unique needs and concerns. These may be related to the matter under investigation, or to external matters. A victim, witness or suspect may have suffered severe trauma at the time of an offence and require some counselling before an interview can take place. Police officers are usually untrained in counselling techniques but can assist the process by simply allowing the interviewees to talk and get the matter off their chest. Others may not have suffered trauma but have important domestic commitments, such as a requirement to return home at a given time as the children are due home from school. The officer who takes the time to identify this and act upon it is much more likely to receive co-operation.

Until these matters are addressed it is unlikely that any form of proper communication can take place, and officers who do not take the time to identify the interviewee's immediate needs and concerns are unlikely to succeed in the interview.

The treatment of an arrested person should be no less courteous than that of a victim or witness. Considerate treatment over and above that required by law can provide dividends. Allowing a suspect the time to wash and dress properly before travelling to the police station may seem relatively unimportant to an officer eager to press on with an investigation, but it may be of extreme importance to the dignity of the prisoner.

As far as is possible, a suspect should be kept informed by the investigator of the progress of the investigation and the likely outcome. Custody office staff have a statutory obligation in respect of this, but investigating officers should not ignore the fact that they too have a duty towards their prisoners and not assume that this is the responsibility of others.

Interviewers who take the time to find out individual needs and concerns, and take steps to address them, are much more likely to succeed in interviews than those who either do not take the time to identify them or choose to ignore them.

Understanding the feelings of the interviewee

Witnesses', victims' and suspects' attitudes toward police interviewers will be affected by the nature of the matter under investigation, their role in the investigation, and their individual personality or character. A victim who has suffered a traumatic event, or a person who has witnessed it, will often be suffering the effects of that stressful experience. A person under arrest may feel isolated or threatened. They may fear the consequences of the alleged offence, or harmful treatment by the police. In even the most routine cases, interviewees may feel nervous and ill at ease in the presence of a police officer.

Successful interviewers develop the ability to understand how individuals feel in these situations and show by their actions that they understand. Interviewees are much more likely to respond to an officer who displays an understanding of how they feel. One of the most useful tools for the interviewer is the ability to empathise, which means to project oneself into the other person's shoes. All feelings are subject to personalities and it is not just for interviewers to try to understand how they themselves would feel if they were in the particular situation. Empathy is to try to understand how individual suspects, witnesses or victims feel in that particular situation, depending on their individual personalities.

Interviewers must remain impartial and objective throughout the whole interview and for this reason we must not confuse empathy with sympathy. Sympathy also requires an understanding of how a person is feeling, but this is usually accompanied by a feeling of wanting to do something about it. There is a great difference between showing that you understand how a person is feeling, and revealing that you feel sorry for them. The interviewer who sympathises with the interviewee is likely to become emotionally involved and possibly lose control of the interview.

Empathy is to understand how the other person feels while maintaining an objective stance.

Explain the reason for the interview

Once introductory matters have been completed and rapport is beginning to develop between the interviewer and interviewee, the interviewer should explain the reason for the interview.

The reason for interviews with some suspects may be to allow them the opportunity to give their account in answer to the allegations against them. In order for them to do this they must be made aware of what they are accused. This does not mean that they should be told all the evidence, but sufficient to allow them the opportunity to give their response to it.

Witnesses and victims also require an explanation of the reason for the interview. The reason for an interview with a witness or victim may be to obtain as much information as possible concerning their knowledge of the matter under investigation.

> *The importance of the interviewee's knowledge in assisting the investigation should be emphasised, in order for interviewees to identify their crucial role in the investigation and appreciate what is required of them.*

Explain the procedures to be followed

The Codes of Practice for the tape recording of police interviews provide the procedures to be followed in relation to suspects and, on commencing an interview, the interviewer must outline those procedures.

Interviewers may choose to make notes during an interview with a suspect, even though it is being tape recorded, and there are many advantages in doing so. It may strike the suspect as unusual for notes to be taken during a tape recorded interview and it may be helpful to explain the reason for this. The purpose of note taking is to allow the interviewer to remember what is said and, at intervals, to summarise back to the interviewee, checking for accuracy and correct understanding without reference to the tape.

Again a witness may be curious for the reason for a written statement, and it can be explained that the purpose of this is to record the witness' evidence so that informed decisions can be made by the police or prosecuting authorities regarding what action is appropriate on the evidence available. If court action is deemed appropriate, the statement will be used as a guide by the prosecutor - and in certain circumstances the statement may be used rather than the witness having to give verbal evidence in court.

The relationship between an interviewer and an interviewee will be significantly enhanced when the interviewee has a full understanding of the procedures to be followed. Once the interviewee understands that there are good reasons for the routines, and accepts they must be followed to make best use of his information, his understanding can contribute to information of a higher quality.

Describe the format of the interview

Interviewers should explain to suspects, witnesses and victims how the interview will be structured:

- firstly the interviewee will be invited to give an account in his own words of the matter under investigation;
- the interviewer will then seek to clarify the account by asking supplementary questions;
- the interviewee will next be asked to comment on any additional matters which have not been covered or adequately explained;
- the interviewer will summarise what has been said at appropriate times to check for correct interpretation.

Difficult interviewees

It is often said that police interviews are not unique in that they have a similar structure to those carried out by doctors, personnel officers, and other professionals. But rarely will those professionals experience the same level of hostility, deceit and often unwillingness to speak at all.

However, even in the case of the most difficult subjects, a great deal can be done by police interviewers to create an atmosphere which will change the other's behaviour and encourage a flow of information. Often interviewers' inappropriate reaction to hostility or resistance can worsen the situation, and they should aim to manage their own behaviour in such a way that it is most likely to help achieve their objectives.

Hostility

Hostility can occur, not only in the case of suspect interviews, but also in the case of witness and victim interviews because it is not everyone's desire to fully co-operate with the police. Hostility or resistance should not always be regarded as a symptom of the person's guilt as it may arise from the righteous anger of an innocent person.

Dealing with hostility requires cool professional conduct by interviewers. Should the interviewer lose patience and return hostility, the interviewee may achieve his aim of terminating the interview, but the interviewer fails in his aim of gaining information. Interviewers who respond in an emotional manner and allow their own feelings of anger to show will lose control of the situation, which is self defeating. If hostility is not matched with hostility it is difficult for interviewees to sustain it. A more effective tactic is to allow the interviewees' emotions to waste their energy, then recommence the interview in a cool manner.

> *Hostility can often be defeated by patience and cool professional behaviour on the part of the interviewer.*

Liars

When an interviewee tells a lie there is a natural tendency for interviewers to challenge the lie immediately, and analysis of police interview tapes show this is the common reaction of many police officers.

The disadvantage in challenging what appears to be a lie in the early stages of the interview is that it often results in stopping the flow of conversation and no further information can be obtained. A better tactic is to make no judgment at this stage and to allow the interviewee to keep talking. It may transpire that the interviewee was not telling lies but was simply mistaken. To accuse an interviewee of telling lies in these circumstances could cause offence and the interviewee may not wish to communicate further with the interviewer.

When it is suspected that interviewees are being deliberately deceptive, an advantage may be gained in allowing them to continue talking and building their account upon a tissue of lies. Further investigation may disprove the account and discredit the suspect or witness at a later stage. There will be occasions when the interviewer already has evidence that the account being provided is false, but it is still wise practice to allow the interviewee to continue.

Not only should interviewees be allowed to complete their account, but the account should be fully examined before any challenge is made in relation to the lie. This will allow interviewees every opportunity to correct their account if they so desire, and to reinforce the strength of the prosecution case if they do not.

It is a common misconception that lies must be challenged in a raised or aggressively assertive voice. The reality is that this encourages the person being interviewed to mirror the interviewer's behaviour. The result is that it stops communication. Officers should not take offence at a deceptive interviewee as this is a normal and understandable reaction for human beings in some situations. The lie should be challenged at the appropriate part of the interview but the challenge should be made without hostility and in a calm and natural tone of voice.

Interviewers who choose to challenge deceptive interviewees prematurely allow them the opportunity to re-adjust their story according to what they learn from the interviewer. If interviewees choose to dig a hole for themselves there is nothing to be gained in a premature challenge - allow them to continue digging.

Silence

The right of a suspect to remain silent still exists even though the court may draw inference from it in appropriate cases. Part of interview planning is to be prepared for such an event and interviewers should be ready to adopt an appropriate strategy depending upon the individual circumstances of the case. Once again interviewers should not become hostile, as nothing will be achieved and it may further alienate the suspect. It is a suspect's lawful entitlement to remain silent, and hostility from the interviewer does no more than reinforce the desire to remain silent.

The following options are available to the interviewer:
- cease the interview immediately without divulging any evidence;
- continue the interview asking selected questions;
- summarise the evidence and ask the suspect to comment upon it.

Terminating the interview may have advantages on some occasions if it allows the interviewer to continue investigations into matters unknown to the suspect, thereby reducing the opportunity for interference with witnesses or evidence. However, the evidence may have to be disclosed at a later stage in accordance with the rules on advance disclosure.

Officers should bear in mind that inference may be drawn from a suspect's silence only if he has been given the opportunity to comment on the evidence. A court is unlikely to draw inference from his failure to comment upon matters unknown to him.

A useful tactic on some occasions may be to suspend the interview once the interviewee intimates he proposes to exercise his right of silence, but to rearrange it once further inquiries have been completed. It may be that the suspect will wish to respond to questions once he becomes aware of the strength of the evidence - by selected questions being put to him, or by outlining the evidence to him and asking him to give an account of it.

The interviewer's reaction to a suspect's right of silence will depend upon the circumstances of each individual case. When planning interviews, interviewers should consider that suspects may exercise their right of silence and decide upon the action they will take in that event.

Summary

It is the duty of an interviewing officer to obtain the most accurate and detailed evidence possible during an interview, and this will be best achieved by creating an atmosphere in which the person being interviewed feels comfortable and able to communicate freely.

Police officers who make an effort to treat witnesses, victims and suspects as individuals, and with courtesy, consideration and respect, are much more likely to fulfil their objectives than those who do not. The interviewees will often be in a situation they have never experienced before, and the police officer must try to understand how they feel and show a willingness to address their immediate needs and concerns. Procedures must be explained to the interviewees so they fully understand their role in the investigation. Suspects must be accorded the same respect as witnesses or victims, and often their insecurities can be minimised by keeping them informed of the progress of the inquiry as much as is possible.

The skill and professionalism of interviewers will often be determined by their ability to adapt and control their own behaviour in accordance with events as they occur.

Those individuals who choose to continue to be hostile, deceptive, or silent are best dealt with by a strategic approach, and by making best use of the legislation now available to restrict manipulation of the criminal justice process.

CHAPTER 3

QUESTIONING

Introduction

Investigative interviews should be conducted as purposeful and directed conversations with the intention of gaining comprehensive factual information in accordance with the interviewer's aim and objectives. The interviewer must create an atmosphere which will allow the witness, victim or suspect to provide detailed information, and at the same time he must control the interview in such a way as to ensure that irrelevancies are kept to a minimum.

This can only be accomplished if the interviewer has a good understanding of:
- the basic rules of questioning;
- the type of questions useful in an interview and when to use them;
- the management of the information received from questioning;
- the questions which are unsuitable for interviews.

Basic rules of questioning

The interviewer is likely to receive most information from a small number of high quality questions.

Fig 9

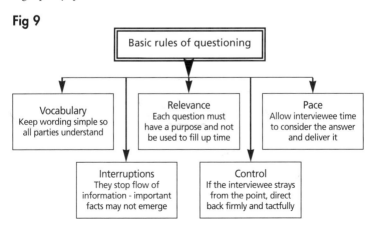

Vocabulary

The wording of questions is important. They should be short, simply worded and relevant to the matter under investigation. Interviewers should aim to put clearly-worded questions which are appropriate to the kind of information required, and are aimed at the intellectual ability of the person who is expected to provide an answer.

Questions can be worded in either a high or a low order. High order questions can make considerable intellectual demands upon interviewees and not everyone is capable of understanding them.

Fig 10

High order and low order questions

High order question: 'Will you give me an appraisal of your current financial situation?'
    Low order question: 'How much money do you have?'

High order: 'Did you realise the inevitable consequences of your actions?'
    Low order: 'What did you expect would happen?'

There is no clear demarcation between high and low order questions, but interviewers should do their best to phrase questions according to the apparent intellectual level of the person being interviewed.

Good questions are worded simply - so that both parties understand them.

Relevance

Many interviews last much longer than necessary because of the tendency of interviewers to go over the same ground repeatedly. Each question must have a purpose, and questions should never be put to fill up the time. It is not necessary to inquire fully into everything that the interviewee says.

A skilled interviewer is able to identify the relevant areas and examine them fully, and does not waste time probing areas from which no relevant information can be gained.

Repetitive questioning is time consuming and unnecessary, and in some circumstances it can result in an interview being ruled oppressive. It could result in all of the interview or a substantial part of it being excluded from evidence in court. Repetitive questions are often an indication of poor interview planning or lack of concentration upon what is being said. Once an interviewer has all the information required then the interview is over, no matter how long it has taken.

A well-prepared interview plan accompanied by listening carefully to everything that is said should eliminate repetitive questioning.

Pace of questioning

The pace of questioning should be carefully controlled as the interviewee must be allowed sufficient time to answer. There is little point in putting questions if the interviewee does not understand what is being said, or is not given the opportunity to reply.

A person being interviewed has to complete the following mental process before he can answer a question:
-   understand the question;
-   think what knowledge he has of the matter;
-   formulate the reply;
-   deliver the answer.

The time required to do this can vary, depending upon a number of factors including the complexity of the issue, the intellectual ability of the interviewee, and whether matters are still fresh in his mind. A deceitful witness or suspect may also require time to compose the lie he intends to tell, but a slow response to a question is not necessarily an indication of falsehood.

Even the simplest of questions requires time to consider the appropriate reply, and if the interviewee is not allowed sufficient time to think about the answer he is likely to provide incomplete and unreliable information. Interviewers must be patient, and be prepared to pause sufficiently long enough to allow time for a considered response to the question. Speed of questioning will not necessarily eliminate deception.

However, analysis of interviews shows that some interviewers seem to believe that the best way to obtain information from a person is to put one question after another without giving sufficient time to reply. Studies also show that interviewers invariably make a good start to the interview by asking a well-phrased open-ended question which invites a detailed account. It then often occurs that when the person does not respond instantly, the interviewer bursts in with a supplementary closed question which cuts the interviewee off prematurely, preventing a detailed answer.

A good open-ended question like 'Will you start from the beginning of the incident and tell me exactly what happened?' invites the interviewee to give a detailed account. While the interviewee is thinking of his answer, and before he has time to respond, the interviewer impatiently interjects, asking: 'What time did you leave the pub?' This confuses the other party who then responds by answering the last question put.

As a consequence, the interviewer strays from his interview plan by continuing with a whole series of closed questions from which limited information will be gained. Valuable additional facts, which would have emerged if the interviewee had been given sufficient opportunity to respond to the first question, may never be revealed. In this example it may be that what happened prior to entering 'the pub' is crucial to the investigation.

> *To interject with a further question while the interviewee is thinking of the answer stops the flow of information and valuable evidence may be lost. Even if the person being interviewed is telling lies there are advantages in allowing the full answer to be given.*

Interrupting the interviewee

Another common fault identified in a study of tape recordings of interviews is for interviewers to interrupt the interviewee after he has started giving his reply. Witness interviews cannot be analysed as readily as suspect interviews, but there is no reason to think they are any different.

Reasons why an interviewee should not be interrupted by the interviewer are:

- it may stop him from disclosing vital information
- it can break his train of thought
- it can impose a bias.

Controlling the interview

One disadvantage in allowing an interviewee to give a free narrative can be that he strays away from matters relevant to the matter under investigation. This can be a particular problem when dealing with an over-talkative witness or suspect. When it appears an interviewee is going off the subject, the interviewer must first of all be sure that what he is saying is immaterial, then calmly and tactfully direct him back to the relevant points.

Fig 11

Bringing the interviewee back to the point

'That's very interesting, but before you continue, can you tell me what happened when you first saw the man acting suspiciously in the street?'

The interviewee should be brought back to the point gently but firmly.

Good questions to use

The type of questions to be used during an interview depends upon the type of response the interviewer requires. If a detailed answer is sought then an open-ended question should be used to encourage an extended response. If an interviewer wants to determine specific points by means of a short specific answer, then a closed question would be more appropriate.

Interviewers who have a clear idea of the various types of question, and when they may be used, will usually succeed in obtaining the information required. A good question is one that encourages the interviewee to provide the information being sought and at the same time motivates him to speak.

Questions are crucial to the success or failure of interviews and interviewers should be able to identify:
  I the difference between good and bad questions;
  I the appropriate question to use at different stages of the interview.

The two main types are open and closed questions. Both are extremely useful to the interviewer but only when used in the appropriate circumstances.

Fig 12

Open and closed questions

Open question: 'Tell me what happened.'
Closed question: 'What time did it happen?'

Open questions

An open question is one that requires the interviewee to respond in detail, and the general concept is that open questions produce open answers. Asking open questions is the best way to encourage interviewees to give a detailed reply and unless the interviewee is being deliberately evasive or obstructive it is almost impossible not to give an open reply. An exception is if the interviewee requires special treatment because of intellectual problems or speech difficulties. In such cases expert help will be available, but it may be necessary to put carefully worded closed questions, making sure the answer is not suggested within the question.

One of the most valuable phrases an interviewer can use is 'Tell me…'. It is valuable because it invites an extended response rather than a simple 'Yes' or 'No' reply.

Examples are:
'*Tell me* what happened.'
'*Tell me* about your movements last Friday evening.'
'Start from the beginning and *tell me* what you saw.'
'*Tell me* about your system of book keeping.'
'*Tell me* what happened next.'
'*Tell me* about the relationship between yourself and the man assaulted.'

The following advantages are to be gained from using open questions:
- the wording encourages interviewees to provide a longer answer which should give more information;
- they allow an interviewee to give a full account in his own words and at his own pace;
- a protracted response requires the person to think more carefully and this will stimulate the memory;
- they allow an interviewer to gain information about areas in which he has little knowledge;
- accounts are less likely to be contaminated by the assumptions of the interviewer;
- the question is neutral and no indication is given to the interviewee of the sort of answer that will win approval - this is particularly important when dealing with persons who may be amenable to suggestion, such as the educationally sub-normal, some young children, or persons with mental difficulties;
- they allow the interviewee to release pent-up emotion or stress if they are nervous, frightened, or have suffered a traumatic experience;
- by encouraging a person to talk, a rough guide may be gained as to his intellectual ability, and this may dictate how the interview should progress and indicate when safeguards may be necessary.

Despite the obvious advantages of open questions, studies of interviews have shown that closed questions are asked more frequently. This is partly because they are more natural to us - we are more likely to use closed questions in normal conversation.

The general rule is that interviews should commence with open questions and gradually progress to closed questions when specific areas need to be clarified.

Part of the planning stage of the interview is to decide upon the first question to put to the person to be interviewed. This is part of the interview plan and it should be written down on the planning sheet. This applies to all interviews whether they be with witnesses, suspects or victims.

Analysis of interviews illustrate that interviewers invariably get the first question right, but are frequently thrown off track when the interviewee does not respond as expected. There are occasions when interviewees hear the question but react by completely ignoring what is asked and responding with what is uppermost in their minds at that time. Those in custody may naturally wish to express their dissatisfaction about being detained, or some other perceived injustice. A victim or a witness of a traumatic event may wish to relieve themselves of pent up emotion.

Fig 13

Typical responses to the opening question of the interview

Q. 'Tell me what happened.'

Suspect's response: 'I have been locked up since six o'clock this morning and I have done nothing wrong.'

Victim's response: 'It was awful, I was terrified, I have never experienced anything like it in my life.'

Witness' response: 'It was a shocking sight - how old was the child who was hit by the car?'

These are perfectly natural responses and there may be merit in the interviewer allowing emotion to be expressed before continuing. However, he should have a second open question in readiness to resume the factual interview when possible, and must resist the temptation to continue with a series of closed questions from which limited information will be obtained.

It may be helpful for the interviewer to write down a secondary opening question on the interview planning sheet in case it is needed.

Fig 14

Secondary open question

Q 'Tell me about your involvement in the offence yesterday afternoon.'
R 'I wasn't there, I didn't do it'

Q 'Well tell me about your movements yesterday.'

An exception to the rule of commencing an interview with an open question may be if the interviewer wishes to prompt the interviewee by providing a starting point. In such cases a direct question may be put to start off the interview at the appropriate point but, once this is determined, the interviewer must revert to open-ended questions to allow the person to respond in more detail.

Fig 15

Prompting question

Q 'What time did you get up this morning?'
R 'Half past seven.'

Q 'Tell me about your movements from half past seven this morning.'

The correct approach for individual interviews will vary depending upon the circumstances of each case, but in some cases providing a starting point for the interviewee may be helpful and the following possible advantages should be considered:

I   in a suspect interview, to explore movements prior to the
    actual commission of an offence may reveal activity of a
    preparatory nature which later becomes vitally important to
    an investigation;

I   to allow an interviewee to begin at a non-contentious point and
    progress chronologically can stimulate the memory and allow for
    more detailed information;

I   a guilty suspect is less likely to claim his right of silence when asked about non-contentious matters, and when the interview progresses to the contentious area it is possible he may continue talking;

▍ it may help in providing an alibi for an innocent suspect.

Extreme care must be taken by the interviewer that the wording of a question does not preclude matters that would have emerged if the first question had been kept entirely open ended.

> *The general rule is that open questions should be used at the beginning of an interview and on introduction of any new topic during the interview. Interviewers should address their thoughts in advance as to the wording of the questions to be used to begin the interview. An interview that gets off to a good start is likely to continue in accordance with the interviewer's aim and objectives.*

Closed questions

Closed questions are also of value during an interview and particularly when there is a need to establish specific information. Closed questions can only be answered within the confines of how the question has been phrased.

Closed questions usually require a short narrowly-confined answer and can be divided into three basic types:

▍ those that can be answered 'Yes' or 'No';

▍ those relating to matters such as quantity, identification or time - 'How many were there?' 'What is your name?' 'What time did it happen?';

▍ those offering a forced selection - 'Did you hit him with a hammer or an axe?'.

Closed questions are normally used after a sequence of open questions and are particularly useful at the probing stage of an interview when more detail and clarification is sought. They would not normally be used at the outset of an interview, or in introducing new topics.

They are also useful when interviewing a person who is inarticulate, or someone of low intellect, as they can reduce embarrassment and help to extract information. In such cases, extreme care must be taken by the interviewer to ensure he does not contaminate the interview with his own assumptions. An appropriate adult should be present and questioning tactics should be discussed prior to the interview.

A further use may be in the case of over-talkative interviewees who introduce irrelevant matters. The strategic use of an appropriately-worded closed question can tactfully steer them back to the point. This tactic should only be used when the interviewer is absolutely sure that what is being said is in fact irrelevant.

The disadvantages of closed questions are that:
- all the stimulation comes from the interviewer and questions are generally restricted to his knowledge of events;
- all the effort comes from the interviewer with little reward in return;
- answers are restricted, so important facts may not emerge;
- little information is received upon which to develop the conversation;
- questions and answers can be delivered and returned like a table tennis match with little opportunity to build up a rapport with the interviewee

Closed questions are very useful in an interview to obtain short, factual answers on specific points, particularly when probing for detail and clarity. However, they should be used sparingly at other times, and rarely in the early stages of an interview.

Managing the response to questions

Once the interviewee responds to questions, the interviewer must be able to manage this response to encourage more information, to expand upon what has been said and to check for accuracy and truthfulness. The interviewer who fails to manage the response to his questions is unlikely to achieve his aim and objectives or to keep control of the interview.

Tactics to manage the information received include:
- showing the interviewee that you are listening and interested in what is being said;
- taking notes during the interview;
- probing for more detailed information;
- summarising what the interviewee says, checking your understanding and accuracy of interpretation.

Showing interest

To encourage continued conversation, the interviewer must not only devote his entire attention to the interviewee but he must also show that he is listening with interest, and that he wants the conversation to continue.

In the normal social context we show we are listening by the occasional nod of the head, maintaining good eye contact, and reassuring comments. If we did not do so the conversation would quickly dry up. The investigative interview is no different and the person speaking, whether he is a witness, victim or suspect, needs some assurance that what he is saying is interesting and relevant. The interviewer who appears sincere and demonstrates his good listening skills will naturally produce the kind of encouragement required.

This subject is therefore of equal relevance to the next chapter on listening skills.

Note taking

The value of note taking will also be mentioned in greater depth in relation to developing listening skills. Notes of an interview are of immense value in assisting the interviewer by providing cues to guide him through the interview, particularly at the probing stage.

The notes should not be allowed to affect the flow of the interview and are by no means a verbatim account of what was said. All that is required is a brief record, often just one key word, of topics you may wish to investigate more fully. The notes have the effect of naturally dividing the interviewee's account into manageable sections, each section to be further developed at the probing stage of the interview.

Fig 16

Example of notes of interview

LEFT HOME
TO SHOPPING PRECINCT
SHOPPING
RETURNED HOME
STAYED IN
WENT TO PUB
RETURNED HOME

Ideally the notes should be printed in fairly large letters so that the interviewer can obtain his cues from them quickly and without interrupting the natural pace of the interview.

Probing

At the start of the interview, the aim is to obtain an account by the use of open-ended questions. No matter how well the interviewee has responded it is unlikely that he has mentioned all he knows. Investigative interviewers must not accept what is said at face value because the interviewee may have forgotten something, may be mistaken, or may be telling lies.

The interviewer makes brief notes dividing the account into manageable parts and when the interviewee has stopped talking it is time to probe what has been said. Each part of the interview must be regarded as a separate objective and probed to expand and clarify the information. By reference to the notes each relevant topic can be fully examined. This is accomplished by the tactical use of both open and closed questions to maximise the information received, and to check for accuracy and truthfulness. Each topic is fully probed before proceeding to the next.

The six key words for successful probing are best illustrated with a quote from Rudyard Kipling:

'I have six honest serving men,
They taught me all I knew,
Their names are What, and Where and When,
and Why and How and Who.'

Fig 17

Probing an objective

Q 'You say you left home in the morning. ***Where*** do you live?'
Q '***How*** long have you lived there?'
Q '***When*** did you leave the house?'
Q '***Who*** was at home when you left?'
Q '***What*** door did you leave by?'
Q '***Who*** saw you leave?'

The interviewer progresses through the interview, probing each objective in turn, until he has fully explored all relevant parts of the interviewee's account. Finally, apparent inconsistencies can be probed as separate objectives.

This should result in a comprehensive and exhaustive account of the interviewee's movements.

Summarising

The main purpose of verbally summarising to the interviewee what has been said is to check the understanding and the accuracy of the interviewer's interpretation.

Summarising has the following advantages:
- it gives the interviewee the opportunity to correct or clarify what has been said;
- it assists the interviewer in ensuring that he has correctly interpreted what has been said;
- it reinforces the interviewer's understanding and helps him to remember;
- it can encourage hesitant interviewees to talk by reassuring them that what is being said is understood and is of interest;
- it makes it difficult for deceptive interviewees to successfully claim in court that they meant something differently.

Fig 18

Summarising

'So what you are saying is:

  that you left the house in the morning and went to the shopping precinct where you did some shopping. You then returned home and stayed in the house all afternoon. During the evening you went to the pub and then returned home and went to bed.

Is that correct?'

The key is to divide the interview into manageable areas and to summarise regularly at the discretion of the interviewer.

The interviewer will normally summarise what has been said at the end if each section of the interview - on completion of the interviewee's initial account, then after dealing with the interview objectives, and finally at the end of the interview. In complex cases it may be necessary to summarise at more regular intervals.

It is up to the interviewers at the planning stage to decide upon what is likely to be the most suitable way to summarise, depending upon the circumstances and complexity of the individual case.

Unsuitable types of question

There are two main types of question that should not be used in any interview as they can either confuse the interviewee or encourage inaccurate information - these are multiple and leading questions.

Multiple questions

A multiple question is worded to contain two or more questions. Such questions are normally put unintentionally rather than deliberately because of the eagerness of the interviewer to gain information. The problem for the interviewee is that he must first of all work out which part of the question to answer.

Not only does it slow the interview down but it can be confusing to both parties involved.

Fig 19

Multiple questions

> **Q** 'What time did you leave the club, and who were you with?'
> **Q** 'Did you hit him deliberately and what were your intentions?'
> **Q** 'Did you see what happened or who struck the first blow?'
> **Q** 'Tell me what night club you went to, who you were with and how much you had to drink.'

A question such as 'Did you see the man climb over the fence and break into the house?' could be answered 'Yes'. This could mean the witness saw the man climb over the fence and break into the house. It could also mean that he saw him climb over the fence, but not break into the house; or break into the house, but not climb over the fence.

Some interviewees may be confident enough to deal with these questions by asking the interviewer which part he wants answered first. Others may answer the part they believe is required, and this could result in answers which are inaccurate and not reflecting the true situation.

The interviewer may be equally confused because he does no know which part of the question is being answered. A further disadvantage is that the guilty suspect or dishonest witness can ignore the part of the question that could lead them into difficulties and answer the part which suits them.

Multiple questions have no use in an interview and should be avoided.

Leading questions

The leading question usually implies an assumption on the part of the questioner, such as: 'You go to public houses often, don't you?' Any value a leading question may have in an interview is heavily outweighed by the dangers of using such questions. They can be perceived by some as suggesting the answer the interviewer would prefer.

Fig 20

Leading questions

  Q 'Several witnesses have referred to a red car leaving the scene. Tell me about it'

  Q 'The man who was taken to hospital struck the first blow - did you see it happen?'

Leading questions may put ideas into an interviewee's head. An uncertain or easily led interviewee may be tempted to confirm matters to please the interviewer, believing that the interviewer knows more about the matter than he himself does.

Leading questions have no value in the investigative interview except at the very end of the interview when summarising what has been said.

Summary

The basic rules of interviewing

√ Questions should be worded simply so both parties understand them.
√ Questions should be relevant to the matter under investigation.
√ Interviewers must pause sufficiently long enough to allow the interviewee to reply.
√ The interviewee must not be interrupted while he is speaking.
√ The interviewer needs to exercise flexibility but also to control the interview in accordance with his objectives.

Questions that are useful to the interviewer

√ Open questions are best for obtaining detailed replies and are particularly useful at the beginning of the interview.
√ Closed questions demand specific information - they are equally useful but normally more applicable later in the interview.

Managing the response to questioning

√ More information will be obtained if the interviewee appreciates that the interviewer is listening and is interested in what is being said.
√ Brief note taking helps the interviewer to structure the interview, provides a reference for probing, and assists recall.
√ An interview should be fully probed using the following key words: ***Where? What? When? Why? How? Who?***
√ Regular summaries allow the interviewee to make corrections, help the interviewer to check his interpretation and understanding, and assist the interviewer in remembering what is said.

Unsuitable questions

✗ Multiple questions are worded to contain at least two separate questions and can only confuse all parties involved.
✗ Leading questions usually assume the answer expected or desired and can result in inaccurate information being disclosed.

The key to good interviewing is have an understanding of the basic rules of questioning accompanied with a sound knowledge of the various types of questions and how to use them, avoiding those questions which should not be used, and managing the information received.

CHAPTER 4

LISTENING

Introduction

There is little point in asking questions if the interviewer fails to listen to what the interviewee is saying, yet this is a common fault with many interviewers. Total concentration is required, but often the interviewer is thinking of the next question, jumping to conclusions, or filtering out information that appears irrelevant. What the interviewer should be doing is listening intently to everything that is said and comparing it with what is already known. An interviewer can not accomplish his task if he fails to identify the significant remark and explore it, or to observe the silence and probe its implications.

Listening skills are therefore essential to an effective questioning strategy. Equally, they are an integral part of managing the response to questions, so this chapter will go on to consider some of the aspects of managing information - note taking and feedback - identified in the previous chapter. The ability of an interviewer to listen effectively can be significantly enhanced by a greater understanding of:

❙ what active listening is;
❙ how it can be improved;
❙ the need for showing interest in what is being said;
❙ the obstacles to active listening.

The nature and value of listening

A confusing distinction for many people is between 'hearing' and 'listening'. Hearing is simply the reception of sound and, while this is obviously an essential element of listening, listening does not always occur along with hearing. An interviewer cannot sit back and expect information to flow into his brain without any effort on his part.

Listening is the process of:

❙ concentrating open-mindedly upon all that is said;
❙ digesting and understanding the information received;
❙ comparing it with what is already known or believed;
❙ remembering.

Fig 21

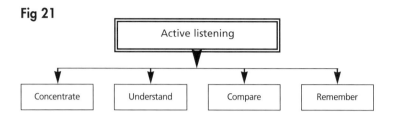

Listening is a complex and demanding task which requires the interviewer's entire concentration and analysis throughout the whole of the interview. It is a valuable skill as it allows the interviewer to accurately interpret the information being provided by the interviewee, and this contributes toward the successful management of the conversation. It enhances the evidential value of the interview and, as important evidential facts emerge, the interviewer is more likely to identify their relevance.

Improving listening skills

More effective listening can be achieved through good practice before and during the interview. Skills can be developed by evaluating interviews after an investigation has been completed in order to recognise where listening skills can be improved. The tape recording of police interviews is an invaluable way of accomplishing this. Most listeners will initially be surprised at the amount of information they missed during the interview.

The following are some suggestions of good interview practice which can help improve listening skills:

▌ carefully select the place of interview whenever possible, with a view to minimising distractions;

▌ employ good preparation and planning prior to the interview - the more knowledge the interviewer has, the more able he is to listen, understand, and remember what is being said - and then compare it with what is already known from other sources;

▌ use two interviewers - one to direct the course of the interview and the other to 'sweep up', covering aspects that may have been missed by the main interviewer;

▌ maintain an open mind throughout the interview - do not jump to conclusions - you may be wrong and mentally filter out important information;

▌ concentrate totally on what is being said - do not think ahead to what the next question should be or what the reply may be;

I limit the amount of talking you do by using concise and meaningful open questions encouraging an extended response from the interviewee - you learn nothing while you are talking;

I give feedback - encourage response by demonstrating to the interviewee that you are listening attentively;

I take notes during the interview - this helps you to remember;

I do not uncritically accept the account you receive - compare it with what is already known or believed and expand upon it, probing the account you are given to test for accuracy and truthfulness;

I periodically verbally summarise back to the person being interviewed what has been said to ensure you have a full and accurate understanding.

Fig 22

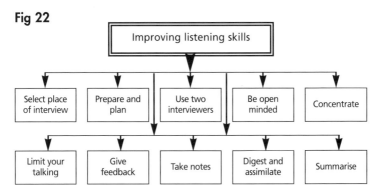

It is useful to consider some of these aspects in more detail.

Taking notes

Opinions vary on taking notes during interviews, as some interviewers feel it detracts from the flow of conversation. Nevertheless, remembering everything that is said can present difficulties to many interviewers and recollection can be vastly improved through note taking.

It is up to individual interviewers to select their chosen method of note taking, but to write down everything verbatim does interfere with the flow of conversation and diminishes the ability to listen effectively. There is a tendency to concentrate more upon writing down the words used rather than on the sense of what is being said. This may result in a jumble of indecipherable notes of minimal value which even the writer has difficulty in reading.

There are occasions when verbatim notes are required by law, and police officers have no discretion in this, but this should be regarded as an exception to the general rule. Where verbatim note taking is not required by law, a process of simple but disciplined note taking can be developed and, with practice, should not interfere with the general flow of the conversation

The key to effective note taking is not to record every word but to jot down an outline of what is said, as the interviewee speaks, using key words *(as shown in Fig 16, chapt 3, Questioning)*. The key words should be well spaced and written in bold letters. Blocks and circles can be drawn around significant points identifying objectives for further investigation. Many interviewers stop at a convenient part of the interview, maybe just prior to a summary, and review their notes, marking the topics that require probing or clarification.

In any event, once the interviewee has stopped speaking, the interviewer can, by referring to the notes, easily verbally summarise back to him what has been said, to reinforce the interviewer's understanding and to check for accuracy. The notes can then be used to assist in probing the interviewee's account and later to clarify or challenge inconsistencies if this is appropriate.

Some interviewers use the left hand side of the sheet to jot down the main points and the right hand side for elaboration as the account is probed. Whichever method of note taking is adopted the interviewer should, with practice, be able to continue to maintain good eye contact with the interviewee and not interrupt the flow of conversation.

Fig 23

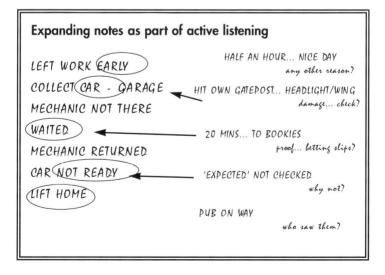

Notes should be taken for both witness and suspect interviews irrespective of whether or not the interview is tape recorded. They can be used for summarising what has been said and allow the interviewer the opportunity to clarify or add information. The notes provide an excellent framework from which to formulate a written statement.

Notes should be taken openly and not surreptitiously and it will help the process if the reason for taking notes is explained at the outset.

The simple system of jotting down brief headings during the interview eliminates the negative aspects of note taking and can lead to greater understanding of what is being said as well as helping to improve recall. It may also assist the interviewer to keep better control of the interview and adhere to a structured but flexible interview plan.

Interviewing in pairs

The availability of resources will often dictate the number of interviewers present at an interview with a witness or suspect, but the involvement of two interviewers can often have clear advantages even if this is simply because two heads are better than one. In complex cases, or when the investigation concerns major crime, this may be particularly advantageous. However, the involvement of more than two interviewers will normally be unnecessary and in some circumstances may appear oppressive.

Interviews involving two interviewers must be strictly managed if they are to be successful. They can otherwise result in interviewers competing, contradicting each other or asking questions repetitively. Before the start of the interview both interviewers should be engaged in the joint planning of the interview strategy.

At the planning stage, the interviewers should agree their respective roles - a main interviewer and a secondary interviewer. A professional approach is necessary and officers should not consider it demeaning to be the second interviewer. Successful investigation involves good teamwork, and monitoring the interview to ensure nothing is missed is a very important role. Often the role of each interviewer may be a natural choice due to one interviewer having a more extensive knowledge of the matter under investigation or of the person to be interviewed.

The interviewers should work as a team, planning and preparing the interview strategy and their respective roles. One method is for the lead interviewer to complete the whole interview and then allow the second interviewer the opportunity to pick up on any points that may have been missed.

An alternative is for the main interviewer to start the interview and to stop at regular intervals, possibly natural breaks, passing over to the second interviewer before introducing the next stage. When this strategy is used, it is important that the second interviewer maintains a disciplined approach by referring only to matters already touched upon in the interview. He must resist the temptation to introduce new topics or stray on to the next stage. Communication between the two interviewers is necessarily limited during the interview, and the second interviewer must be alert as to the possibility that the main interviewer has deliberately left an aspect unexplored as part of a strategy.

Once the second interviewer has completed his task, control should pass back to the main interviewer. The main interviewer then continues through the next sections of the interview, allowing the second interviewer to 'sweep up' after he has probed each of the sections.

The interviewers will have discussed at the planning stage their preference for taking notes during the interview, and some may feel it helpful for both to maintain their own notes rather than try to decipher notes made by the other party. In any event it may be more convenient for the interviewer who is to summarise the account back to the interviewee to maintain notes.

The use of two interviewers is conducive to good interview practice and promotes active listening.

Social reward - encouraging response

An essential part of the interaction is that the interviewer listens to what is being said. However it is also important that he shows to the interviewee that he is listening. If the interviewer appears attentive and interested it encourages the interviewee to continue speaking and impart more and more information. If the interviewer gives the interviewee no feedback, either verbal or non-verbal, the conversation and the flow of information is likely to dry up.

Part of the process of active listening is that the interviewer must continually reward the interviewee with feedback, and it is important that this feedback is appropriate to the circumstances.

Feedback can be positive or negative. A positive response expresses satisfaction, interest or agreement with what is being said, and this may not be appropriate in some investigative interviews, particularly if it is known the interviewee is telling lies. A negative response indicates displeasure and disagreement and such a response may quickly stop the interviewee talking and terminate the flow of information. Even if the interviewee is telling lies it is important that he be allowed to continue.

In many interviews it may be more appropriate to provide feedback that either conveys no judgement or gives an ambiguous or non-committal response.

Maintaining good eye contact with the interviewee indicates without words that you are listening attentively, but does not provide indications of your agreement or disagreement. Defensive bodily postures - such as sitting cross legged with arms crossed over the chest and a blank facial expression - do not encourage co-operation and such postures should be avoided. It is more acceptable for the interviewer to lean forward slightly and towards the interviewee with a more open posture. This should be accompanied by the occasional nod of the head, in encouragement rather than in agreement, and an occasional smile to assure the interviewee that his response is appreciated.

> *More information will be obtained if the interviewee appreciates that the interviewer is listening and is interested in what is being said.*

Obstacles to effective listening

It is important to identify the barriers to effective listening so that they can be avoided. It will often be necessary to conduct interviews in less than ideal circumstances, but the elimination of as many as the negative factors as is possible will help the interview process.

Interview setting

Most police stations now have dedicated interview rooms for suspects, and many police areas have specially-designed interview suites for victims of child abuse and serious sexual offences. Unfortunately not all police stations have adequate arrangements for general witness interviews and often *ad hoc* arrangements have to be made.

Dedicated facilities should be used whenever they can be but, when these are not available, the interviewer should aim to create the best environment possible.

This is so whether the interview is to take place in a police station or one of a variety of other locations. If the environment in which the interview is to take place is noisy, or there are other distractions, it will not be easy for the interviewer or the person being interviewed to concentrate. Interruptions break the thread of the interview and the relationship developed with the interviewee can rarely be recaptured. Whenever possible, the place of interview should be carefully selected, aiming for privacy and an environment where the possibility of distractions and interruptions is minimal.

When an interview is to take place on the interviewee's premises, it may be helpful to explain the advantages of privacy before starting the interview. This may encourage the interviewee to take measures to prevent interruptions and distractions. In the domestic setting this may be no more than arranging for another member of the household to keep the children in another room and switching off the television set for the duration of the interview.

> *The more privacy you can achieve, the more information you are likely to receive, as both the interviewer and interviewee are able to concentrate on the subject matter.*

Mental inhibitors

The interviewer should be able to devote his entire attention to the interview throughout its duration. The average person is capable of listening as much as four times faster than a person talks. The extra thinking time allows for mind wandering and this is a barrier to effective listening. Mind wandering can arise because of matters unconnected with the interview such as professional and personal pressures. It can also involve other trains of thought connected to the interview - a common one is planning ahead to the next question as the interviewee answers the last one.

When interviewing, all factors that intrude and demand extra mental activity should be left outside the interview room. Good preparation and a well-prepared interview plan should eliminate the need to think ahead to the next question.

> *Mind wandering is one of the most seductive of listening barriers which severely impairs effective listening and the result can be that important evidential facts may be missed by the interviewer.*

Pre-conceived ideas

An interview should always be approached with an open mind. Forming pre-conceived ideas or jumping to conclusions during the interview can have equally detrimental effects upon the interviewer's ability to listen. Interviewers who jump to conclusions hear only what they want or expect to hear, other information is filtered out as the interviewer selectively perceives messages. The result is that valuable information can be lost.

Only after a full account has been given will the interviewer sift the required facts from those that appear irrelevant. Even so, apparent irrelevancies should be filed in the mind for future reference as they may become relevant as the interview progresses. The open minded interviewer is more likely to recall them.

A good interviewer enters the interview room with an open mind and maintains an open mind throughout.

Lack of understanding

When an interviewer does not fully understand the matter being investigated it severely impairs his ability to listen effectively. He is unable to make sense of or manage the information received, and the reality is that no effective communication can take place.

This can normally be overcome by good preparation, thereby making sure the interviewer is aware of all pertinent facts prior to the interview. Preparation and planning has been explored in chapter one but, to recap, the absolute minimum should consist of:

- attending the scene of the offence and becoming familiar with all aspects, including the geographical situation;
- speaking to available witnesses, including colleagues;
- studying all available statements and other documentation relevant to the investigation;
- getting to know as much as is possible about the interviewee before commencing the interview.

A fully-prepared and knowledgeable interviewer is more able to understand what he is being told, and this enables him to listen more attentively, identifying the important points of the conversation and differentiating between the relevant and non-relevant facts.

Summary

This chapter has illustrated the nature and value of listening, the obstacles to effective listening, the measures that can be adopted to enhance listening skills and the need for social reward.

The guide to good listening can be summarised as follows:

√   Give careful consideration to where the interview takes place using a dedicated interview room whenever possible - when this is not possible strive to achieve the best possible environment so that both interviewer and interviewee can fully concentrate upon the matter at hand.

√   Prepare and plan before the interview - if time is at a premium use the time that is available to best advantage.

√   Consider the use of two interviewers - work together with a disciplined approach to a common interview plan.

√   Be open-minded - do not enter the interview with pre-conceived ideas and do not jump to conclusions.

√   Concentrate upon what is being said - do not think ahead as to what the likely answer may be, or the next question to put.

√   Take positive action to eliminate obstacles to active listening - keep the mind firmly upon the subject matter.

√   Show interest in what is being said - even if you do not believe it.

√   Take notes - the notes of the interview assist the interviewer to remember what is said and manage the information.

√   Assimilation - digest information as it is received and compare it with what is known or believed.

√   Summarise regularly what the interviewee is saying to check for accuracy of interpretation and understanding.

Listening is more than hearing - it means focusing, perceiving and assimilating. Good listening produces higher quality information, which is the key to good interviewing and professional and successful investigation.

It is up to individual interviewers to improve listening ability, and this is best achieved by evaluating one's own performance and making a conscious effort to adopt the appropriate strategies to strengthen any areas of weakness.

Interviewers should listen to their own tape-recorded interviews after completion of the investigation to identify the points that were missed. Those who take the time to do this will be surprised at what they find, and also how rapidly their ability to listen will be improved.

PART TWO

STRUCTURING INTERVIEWS

CHAPTER 5

INTERVIEWING WITNESSES

Introduction

The concept of developing police officers' investigative interviewing skills was virtually unknown until the introduction of tape recorded suspect interviews during 1984. Even then police training courses focused mainly on interviewing suspects with little more than cursory attention to the skills required for interviewing witnesses and victims.

The development of skills in interviewing witnesses and victims is of equal importance to that for interviewing suspects because reliable witness evidence is of immense value to any investigation. Not only is this the case for routine day-to-day investigations but also computerised systems for the management of serious crime rely heavily on the accurate recording of evidence from potential witnesses in the form of written statements. Fortunately police training courses have been improved to develop officers' skills in interviewing both witnesses and suspects.

In an ideal world a witness would be an intelligent and articulate individual who could relate to the police a comprehensive and accurate account of what they had seen - but this is often not the case. Police officers must be able to deal with a diverse range of personalities including those who have difficulty expressing themselves, are unable to recall events accurately, or have intellectual problems. Special skills are necessary to coax factual information from some people.

The attitude of witnesses can differ. Some may be completely impartial and willing to provide an honest and accurate account of what has transpired, but others may be motivated by malice or otherwise intent upon deliberately providing false and misleading information.

It is important for interviewers to identify those who would wish to pervert the course of justice but it is also important to be open-minded and not to prematurely assume that a witness is being untruthful if an apparent inconsistency arises. A witness may be mistaken in his interpretation of some aspect of what has occurred, but able to provide accurate information in relation to other aspects. In any event a premature challenge should be avoided. A simple mistake may later be rectified or a deceitful witness continue to reveal himself as such.

Some witnesses may be emotional at the time of an interview as a result of the trauma of their experience. However, while interviewers must treat all interviewees with sensitivity, they must at the same time objectively consider what has been said. Information obtained during the interview should not be accepted at face value and interviewers must be impartial throughout, not allowing their judgement to be clouded by emotion or bias. Witnesses and victims may ultimately be required to give evidence in court where their account will be scrutinised in much greater detail. Weaknesses in a witness' testimony should be identified before it reaches that stage of the proceedings.

The term 'victim' can be an emotive one but victims of offences are also witnesses and for the purpose of investigative interviewing the two should be regarded as synonymous.

> *The overall purpose of the interviewer in dealing with a victim or a witness is the same - to obtain accurate, relevant and factual information.*

Initial encounter

Members of the public and other persons who have information about an offence usually have nothing to gain personally by involving themselves as witnesses for the police. Conversely they may have to give up a significant part of their personal time by being interviewed and providing a witness statement. They may later be required to attend court, often in such circumstances that they may feel they have been given less consideration than the accused person.

They may have to:
I   confront the accused person;
I   give evidence in the presence of the offender's relatives and supporters;
I   face the accused, his friends or his family after the proceedings are over;
I   feel responsible for the possible punishment of the alleged offender.

Considering these disadvantages it is surprising that most people, if approached correctly by the police, are willing to involve themselves in the criminal justice process. Much depends upon the police officer's manner in the initial encounter with the witness as it will greatly influence their willingness or otherwise to co-operate. The initial encounter may also affect the quality of the person's evidence as an incorrect approach may irreparably contaminate the evidence the witness can provide.

Potential witnesses should always be treated with courtesy and consideration. Whenever possible the interview should start by the interviewer explaining:

| the reasons for the interview;
| what is expected of the interviewee;
| the procedures that will be followed.

In a spontaneous situation, such as arrival at a scene of crime shortly after the commission of the offence, it may not be appropriate to embark on a lengthy explanation before asking the witness what has happened, but a brief explanation may be helpful.

Police officers should be constantly aware of a simple formula for obtaining information from a witness without contaminating the account:

What? Where? When? Why? How? and Who?

After a brief introduction the interview may be as follows:

| *What* happened?
| *Where* did it happen?
| *When* did it happen?
| *How* did it happen?
| *Why* did it happen?
| *Who* did it?

This simple sequence of questions can provide the key to obtaining an extensive initial account of what has occurred. The opening question allows for an uncontaminated account from the interviewee and the subsequent questions allow for elaboration without contamination.

Once the officer has received this information it should be sufficient to determine the action required and to commence the investigation. This may amount to communicating the information to other personnel, arresting an offender, or any other immediate action that is considered necessary. Arrangements can also be made for a formal interview at a more suitable place and time.

The attitude of an officer arriving at the scene of an offence is extremely important. Witnesses may well mirror the officer's attitude and so a positive approach and professional manner are essential. An officer portraying a negative image, for example, 'There is little point in arresting them, the courts just let them off', will not encourage a positive response from witnesses or inspire them with confidence in the officer.

Police officers need to take command of an incident, communicating an enthusiastic attitude toward successful investigation. A potential witness needs to feel that effort will be worthwhile, appreciated and likely to be acted upon by the police. The witness may well understand the problems of shortage of police manpower and that courts may not always deal with offenders as we would wish, but this is not the time, if ever, to express such negative views.

> *A professional and positive image displayed by a police officer inspires confidence and respect, and this is likely to result in the co-operation of those able to contribute to the investigation, as they will feel it to be a worthwhile exercise.*

Considerations prior to the interview

Where should the interview take place?

Before starting the interview, consideration should be given to the environment in which it is to be conducted. The goal of obtaining accurate, factual and relevant information can be best achieved if the interviewer has made an effort to provide an environment in which the process can evolve naturally. The more witnesses feel comfortable in their surroundings the more likely they are to concentrate upon the demanding task before them of disclosing all the information they have relating to the matter under investigation. Often occasions will arise when officers have to conduct interviews in much less than ideal situations, but the officer who does not at least try to create the best possible environment for the interview will fail in his role as a good investigator.

In ideal situations it will be possible to arrange interviews by appointment at an appropriate place convenient to all persons concerned. On many other occasions interviews will be spontaneous and the environment will be restrictive. The amount of time available prior to an interview and its location will vary according to individual circumstances, but interviewers should strive to find a place as free as possible from distractions where both parties can concentrate upon the task in hand.

In the case of a spontaneous, high-priority or emergency incident with officers hurriedly attending the scene, the best place for an interview may be seated in a vehicle rather than standing in the street. It will usually be possible to obtain as much basic information as necessary while at the scene in order to deal with most pressing inquiries, but to postpone the formal interview to a more suitable venue.

If an interview is to take place in a home, the importance of privacy free from distractions should be explained to the householder who may be able to provide a room separate from other occupants. Where this is not possible the householder should be encouraged to switch off the television and remove as many other distractions as possible. When there are children present it may be possible to ask a neighbour or relative to look after them for the duration of the interview.

Should the interview be on business premises, private facilities should be requested where there is no likelihood of the interview being interrupted by members of staff, incoming telephone calls, or other distractions.

Witnesses may be interviewed in specially designated interview rooms at police stations, hospitals or victim support premises. Lengthy or complex interviews should always, if in any way possible, be carried out where such facilities are available so that everyone involved concentrates their thoughts on the matter under investigation.

In all cases interviews should take place at the most suitable location available, and the interviewer should take measures to eliminate or minimise the possibility of distractions or interruptions.

When should the interview take place?

The time of interview is an important factor and, when there is a choice, the interviewer should try to arrange a time suitable to all parties concerned. The general rule is that witnesses should be interviewed at the earliest possible opportunity while matters are still fresh in their minds.

Officers should be aware that witnesses who have pressing engagements are unlikely to be able to devote their entire attention to relating a detailed account of what happened and then providing a statement. Some witnesses may agree to a suggestion which is inaccurate or untrue simply to get away and fulfil their commitments. Police officers may have similar pressures and should not embark upon interviewing a witness unless they have sufficient time to do so.

Special procedures exist for situations in which the witness has suffered a recent traumatic experience. An intensive interview with a traumatised person will usually result in unreliable and misleading information, as well as causing further unnecessary distress to the person concerned. Once the shock of an ordeal has subsided they will be more likely to recall events and provide accurate and factual information.

In the past, victims of serious sexual offences were required to attend a police station immediately the offence was reported, regardless of the time of day or night. They were required to remain there until a medical examination, interview, and lengthy written statement were completed and this often took several hours. Investigating officers were usually well-intentioned in wanting to investigate serious offences expeditiously but the result was invariably a wholly inaccurate written statement as well as creating further unnecessary distress to the victim. A consequence was that the victim became an easy target for defending lawyers when matters were recalled differently in court. Victims, even though truthful, were easily discredited. Ironically it was the account given in court which was usually the more accurate one.

A more suitable option is for an officer to obtain a brief account from the victim of what has happened at an early stage, and to fully interview them only after they have been allowed an adequate period of rest and when the stressful condition has significantly diminished.

An initial account is important, as inquiries should be made as soon as possible after an offence is reported. There is no reason why the initial account should not be tape recorded - provided the victim agrees - and the recording can be of immense value to investigating officers at an early stage of an inquiry. (The tape recorder is a valuable tool to the interviewer and should be used to full advantage, not just for interviews with suspects. The tape recording should later be subject to disclosure to the defence in the event of court proceedings.) It is emphasised that the initial interview should be no more than a brief account, the probing being left to a more suitable time. If other professionals are present providing medical or counselling services, they must be consulted before attempting the interview.

> *The general rule is that witness interviews should take place at the earliest possible opportunity (with the above provisos in mind) so that uncontaminated information can be obtained while the matter is fresh in their minds.*

Who should conduct the interview?

Another consideration is who should conduct the interview. Investigation often requires good teamwork and police officers should be ready to accept that there are situations when they are not the best person to conduct an interview. A professional approach is necessary and it should not be considered derogatory when a decision is made to appoint others who are believed to be better suited to carry out the interview. After all, an officer lacking training in scientific examination would not consider examining a scene of crime for forensic evidence; neither would an untrained officer consider he should be involved in a tactical firearms operation or take the place of a dog handler in searching an area for offenders. In some situations interviews with witnesses and victims require skills that are of a comparative standard to those required in many other specialist fields.

Some police forces now have dedicated interviewers trained to deal with special categories of offences. Officers attending incident scenes and recognising when a specialist interview is appropriate should take care not to contaminate the account by asking leading or suggestive questions. For operational reasons it may be necessary to obtain a brief account, but all that may be required is for the officer to say: 'Tell me what happened.' The officer should make a note of the account provided to assist with the subsequent investigation. Extensive probing of the account should be left to the specialist interviewer. The initial notes can be passed to the specialist interviewer at a convenient time.

There will be other occasions when investigators consider themselves not to be the best person to conduct an interview - maybe when there has been some conflict between themselves and the person who is to be interviewed. The conflict may have arisen at an earlier stage of the investigation or in a previous unrelated incident. The priority of officers should be to adopt the tactics which are most likely to advance the investigation.

> *The best person to conduct an interview is the person who has the greatest chance of achieving the desired result.*

Preparation and planning

Preparation and planning has already been mentioned in some depth but its importance is so vital to effective interviewing that it is worth briefly mentioning it again specifically in relation to witness interviews.

The more information interviewers have prior to the interview, the more able they will be to maintain control of the interview ensuring it goes in the right direction. The interviewer should try to gain as much background information as possible before the interview. The time available will vary, but the time that is invested in preparation and planning will vastly improve the confidence and the ability of the interviewer and, in the long term, save time.

An interviewer who is knowledgeable will be in control of the situation and much more likely to gain the maximum amount of relevant and factual information.

The background information may be about the offence and about the person to be interviewed. It is essential that interviewers make every effort to visit the scene before the interview to familiarise themselves with the area and what has occurred. There will often be occasions when it is strongly advisable to attend the scene with the witness. The character of the person to be interviewed is relevant but the interviewer must always maintain an objective approach. A person with a previous history of criminal conduct may not necessarily be giving a false account, and a person of apparently impeccable character may not necessarily be telling the truth. A thief can be victim of theft, a robber victim of robbery and prostitutes are extremely vulnerable to rape.

The interviewer should read all available statements and any other documentation, speak to important witnesses and officers who initially attended the scene, examine exhibits or other material evidence, and be aware of similar incidents or offences that may be related.

> *The greater the knowledge an interviewer has of the offence and the parties involved, the greater is his ability to listen effectively to the witness and to evaluate what is being said.*

Conducting the interview - five stages of interview

> *Interviews with both suspects and witness can be divided into five identifiable stages. However the stages are not exactly the same for each and this difference reflects the different emphasis of the witness and suspect interview.*

The emphasis of the witness interview is on examining the account in detail to extract the maximum information. The five stages of the witness interview are:

1. Starting the interview - explanation of procedures.
2. Obtaining the witness' initial account.
3. Expanding the witness' account.
4. Dealing with the interviewer's objectives.
5. Review.

Explaining procedures, obtaining the initial account and dealing with the interviewer's objectives will usually involve the same process regardless of the kind of information the witness is believed to have, but the means of expanding the account will vary. The strategy used will depend upon the type of situation the interviewee has witnessed.

Choosing the right strategy

The interviewer must be prepared to encourage the witness to expand the account by the best means to gain as much information as possible. There are two ways in which this can be accomplished and the interviewer must carefully consider the tactics that are most appropriate in the circumstances.

The method used depends on whether the person is a witness in relation to:
  a. a live event - an eye witness to a robbery, road traffic accident, or other live incident;
  b. a factual matter other than a live event - such as a formal report of a burglary from the victim who has not witnessed it; a sequence of

events concerning the movements of a suspected person; or a system of bookkeeping;

When the witness has been eye witness to a live event it will be beneficial to try to encourage them to re-live the incident by recreating the situation in their mind as though it was actually happening again. The witness who is able to mentally visualise the event as though it were actually occurring will usually be able to provide a much better recollection of events.

When the purpose of the interview is to seek factual information other than eye witness evidence, it will usually be sufficient for the police officer to obtain the information required by the use of open-ended questions to encourage a free narrative from the witness to enlarge their initial account.

Fig 24

The five stages of the witness interview

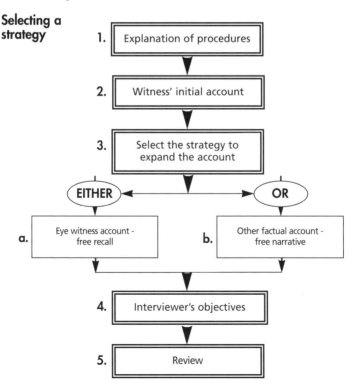

Selecting a strategy

1. Explanation of procedures

2. Witness' initial account

3. Select the strategy to expand the account

EITHER ← → OR

a. Eye witness account - free recall

b. Other factual account - free narrative

4. Interviewer's objectives

5. Review

1. Starting the interview - explaining procedures to the witness

Witnesses who feel insecure and uncertain are unlikely to be able to face up to the demanding task ahead of them - of devoting their entire attention to the matter under investigation and imparting detailed, accurate information to the interviewer. It is the job of the interviewer to help remove these insecurities and uncertainties by ensuring the witness fully understands what is to take place and the reason for it. The most effective way of accomplishing this is for the interviewer, once the introductory formalities have been dealt with, to take the time to explain fully the purpose of the interview, the procedures to be carried out, what is expected of the witness and the possible consequences of their involvement with the police.

What are the reasons for the interview? The reasons for interviewing the witness are to ascertain exactly what has happened; to determine the involvement of the parties concerned, and to make informed decisions as to what action should be taken.

How will the interview be structured? The structure of the interview should enable the interviewer to ask the witness to give their account of the matter under investigation and then to ask questions that may be necessary to enlarge upon the account and to clarify it.

What is required of a witness ? The requirements of the witness will be to totally concentrate their mind upon what has occurred and provide an accurate, factual and unbiased account of it.

The witness should be instructed as follows:

I   concentrate on the incident;
I   be ready to work hard to recall what happened;
I   take as much time as necessary - do not try to hurry, and
    speak slowly;
I   try to provide as much detail as possible;
I   do not miss out anything no matter how immaterial it may seem as
    every piece of information is vital;
I   be prepared to go over the incident several times to assist the recall process;
I   work as a team with the interviewer towards a common purpose;
I   feel free to ask questions at any stage if unsure of anything.

What is the purpose of a written statement? At the end of the interview the witness may be asked to give a written statement so that the available evidence can be considered by the Crown Prosecution Service or others involved in the prosecution process. The purpose of the statement is to allow informed decisions to be made as to what further action should be taken. During the interview the interviewer will take notes as the witness speaks and later use these notes to assist in writing down the statement.

What is likely to happen? The consequences of an interview may be that the person against whom an offence is alleged may be prosecuted or dealt with by some other means. The witness may be required to give evidence in court and the prospect of this should be realistically described to the witness. In practice witnesses are required to give evidence in court in only a small proportion of cases. When attendance in court is necessary, most areas now have special arrangements for caring for their safety and welfare. Officers should use their judgement in realistically assessing the consequences for witnesses and take care not to jeopardise proceedings by making promises that may not be fulfilled.

2. Obtaining the initial account from the witness

All interviews should begin with the witness being asked to tell, in their own words and in their own time, exactly what they saw. The aim is to obtain the maximum amount of relevant factual detail from the witness' version of what has occurred. The usual way of achieving this is by putting a brief open-ended question to encourage an extended response. The question should be so worded as to direct the witness to what information is required and invite them to tell the interviewer everything they know in relation to it. The wording of the question will vary depending upon individual circumstances but the following are common examples.

Fig 25

Opening question

'I understand you witnessed a robbery in Gillbridge Avenue yesterday afternoon? *Tell me* what you saw.'
'In relation to the attack on you last Friday night, *tell me* what happened.'

A well-worded open-ended question allows witnesses the opportunity to give a comprehensive response in their own words and in their own time. The extent of the response will vary depending upon the personality of the witness and the nature of the matter under investigation. There will be occasions when the interviewee's response is inadequate and this may be particularly so when the person is less articulate, or nervous. The interviewer should resist the temptation to revert to closed questions to guide the witness, but instead be ready to put a supplementary open-ended question.

Fig 26

Opening question followed by supplementary question

Q 'I understand you witnessed a handbag snatch in Millbank last Thursday evening? Tell me what happened.'

    R 'It was all over very quickly, I did not get a good look at the man who did it, it was dark.'

Q 'I understand that, but start from the beginning and tell me what you did see.'

This second open question allows the witness to concentrate his mind on what he did see and explain it in his own words.

Had the interviewer reverted to closed questions, which is a common fault with many police interviewers, the information received would normally be less extensive. Furthermore the account could be contaminated by the wording of the questions or the interviewer unwittingly introducing his own pre-conceived ideas.

When the witness is answering the question, interviewers should refrain from interruption and should say nothing other than to indicate that they are listening and interested in what is being said. In particular, the interviewer should not challenge any inconsistencies or even apparent lies, because to do so may have the effect of causing the witness to discontinue the conversation. It may be that the witness is mistaken in some respect and an early challenge may be construed as an allegation of untruthfulness. A better tactic is to allow the witness to continue talking and to deal with inconsistencies or apparent lies at the end of the interview. Should the interviewee become reticent at that late stage much less information would be lost.

Once the initial account has been received the interviewer must move on to the next stage which is to encourage the witness to elaborate upon the account, hopefully providing much more extensive information.

3. Expanding the account

It is at this stage of the interview that the tactics will vary as to how the account is to be expanded. When the interviewer is dealing with a witness other than an eye witness, the interview should continue by further open-ended questions, then progress to more direct questions until the all the required information has been received. In cases where the witness has experienced a live event then very different tactics are necessary.

3a. Expanding the eye witness account - free recall

It is not necessary here to delve into the complex depths of psychological theory and practice by describing advanced techniques used by certain professionals to enhance a person's recollection of events - although there is some merit in a small core of police officers being trained in such techniques.

Most police officers require no more than a rudimentary and common sense understanding of:
- how the memory works;
- the matters that may have a detrimental effect upon the recollection of events by a witness;
- a knowledge of practical tactics which can assist an interviewee in recalling greater detail of incidents they have witnessed.

It is widely known that our aptitude to recall fine detail of occurrences and events can be affected by our intellectual ability, and that memory can diminish as we get older - but there are recurring events that affect all of us in our ability to recall intricate detail. The memory is not total, but is selective, and in the normal course of daily events the subconscious mind considers some matters are unnecessary or unwanted and they are filtered out.

An example of filtering out information may be the routine journey we take to get to work each day. We set off knowing which way we will travel and our intention is to reach work on time safely, but when we arrive at our destination our recollection of how we got there can be vague. We will have passed traffic lights, negotiated roundabouts, avoided other vehicles and pedestrians, but exactly how we did this is unclear when we later try to recall it. The reason is that our journey has been accomplished by habit, and our mind has filtered out many aspects which were not only routine but, in the subconscious mind, immaterial. Should some unexpected or unusual event have occurred it is likely we would quickly devote our entire attention to it and may record it vividly in our memory.

An experience that can adversely affect our ability to recall information accurately is trauma or excitement. The victim of a sudden violent attack is more likely to be thinking of self-preservation than trying to remember everything that occurs. It is common for victims of serious sexual offences and witnesses of traumatic incidents to be so affected that they have difficulty in recalling everything that happened. Generally, the sooner we are asked to recall events the more likely we are able to remember fine detail, but an exception may be the person who has gone through a traumatic experience. In these cases it may be beneficial to wait until the excitement or terror of the incident has subsided so that the witness can concentrate with a more stable mind.

The ability of a witness to recall information can be improved by encouraging the person to apply more concentration. Tactics can be used which in most cases are likely to result in more information being revealed - and it should not be assumed that these tactics are to be used only in complex or serious cases. They should be used in all cases, serious or not, where it is necessary to encourage a witness to expand upon certain aspects of the information provided. Indeed there is merit in police officers practicing these tactics at every possible opportunity until the process becomes natural, and they will be no stranger to it when the important case arises.

The interviewer will have obtained an initial account of the incident in the usual way and it is now time to expand the account in the hope of revealing more detailed evidence.

The interviewer must first of all set the scene by explaining to the witness that it may help their recollection of events if they imagine the incident is happening again and they are experiencing it anew. By the witness imagining they are back at the scene and experiencing the event, it will help them focus their mind to remember in greater detail exactly what happened.

The technique relies heavily upon the interviewer being able to convince the interviewee that the method works and gaining maximum co-operation. Before starting to use this method of encouraging a more detailed account, the interviewer must explain the technique in a positive and convincing manner, possibly mentioning occasions when it has been successful in the past. Once the interviewer is confident that the witness is ready to proceed he should start by giving a resumé describing the witness' presence at the scene. The starting point may be at the beginning of the incident or maybe at another appropriate point of the incident where the expansion is required. Once this is established the interviewer should ask the witness to relate what they can see.

Fig 27

Example

'So you are standing at the bus stop about 9.00pm. It is raining heavily, it is cold, and you are concerned because you are going to be late arriving at work. As you look across the road towards the off-licence you see a man running out of the shop carrying a knife. I want you to concentrate upon this and imagine you are standing at the bus stop now and witnessing what is happening. Remember that we require as much information as possible. Tell me what is happening.'

It is important that the interviewer speaks as though the incident is occurring now. Questions should be worded in the present tense, such as 'Tell me what is happening' or 'What can you see?', rather than 'Tell me what happened' and 'What did you see?'. When relating the account the witness may well speak in the past tense but this should not inhibit their ability to recall the incident. Greater detail should emerge and this will illustrate that the person is thinking as though the event is occurring now.

In certain cases it may be beneficial to return to the scene with the witness to re-live the event. Ideally this would be at a time when the situation is such that the witness is able to fully concentrate, but there may be occasions when the interviewer wishes to recreate the scene as realistically as possible. The circumstances of each individual case will dictate the best way of accomplishing this - it may be necessary to return for example at a busy shopping hour or peak traffic period if these are the conditions under which the incident took place.

The witness or victim should be allowed the freedom to move about the scene as they wish, concentrating and reliving the event. The officer should accompany them at all times, if necessary making brief notes of what is said. In some cases protection from the elements or distractions may be of benefit for a time, even if this is no more than the inside of a motor vehicle.

The account given will not normally differ from the initial account except that there should be greater detail and additional points may be recalled giving a fuller picture of what has occurred.

Should the interviewer feels there is merit in allowing the witness to go over the incident again they should do so if it is believed this may result in more information. In particular the interviewer may wish for the witness to again concentrate on certain aspects of the incident in the hope of gaining more detail.

Fig 28

Example

'So, after the man ran out of the shop he jumped into the car? I want you to concentrate upon the car. Now tell me what you see.'

However, the interviewer should be conscious that some witnesses, if pushed too hard, may be tempted to relate matters imagined rather than matters of fact in order to please the interviewer. Care should also be taken not to create the impression that the witness is disbelieved, by explaining to the witness that some repetition may be necessary to extract the maximum information.

It must be emphasised that this is not a theoretical model of interviewing but a highly successful and practical method of obtaining the maximum amount of information from a witness.

Most people have experienced situations in everyday life when they are trying to recall something that has happened and they reflect back, putting themselves at the scene, to think the matter through. It may be an event that they have experienced or simply an occasion when they have mislaid the car keys in the house. Those of us who have experienced such occasions will agree that casting one's mind back to first entering the house and re-living the movements chronologically thereafter is a highly effective way of recalling events.

Note of caution - In some cases it may not be in the interests of the witness' or victim's welfare to encourage them to re-live the event. An example may be if the person concerned has suffered severe trauma. Officers should not hesitate to seek professional advice when they suspect this may be the case.

Fig 29

Expanding the eye witness' account

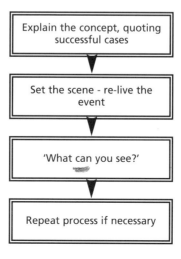

3b. Expanding the factual account - free narrative

The aim of expanding a factual account is identical to that of an eye witness account - to gain the maximum information possible from the witness. However there is no point in a witness who has not witnessed a live event imagining they are at the scene and telling the interviewer what they can see.

Evidence of factual matters other than live events are best obtained with the use of open-ended questions, taking the witness step by step through each aspect of the account they have already given, and probing what they have said. The interviewer will have noted key topics in the form of objectives as the witness related the initial account, and the notes will provide the framework for this part of the interview.

Fig 30

> ## Notes of interview with burglary victim
>
> LEFT HOME
> WENT TO THE CINEMA
> RETURNED HOME
> FRONT DOOR FORCED OPEN
> PROPERTY STOLEN

Breaking down the witness' account into manageable components and asking questions about each component part allows the witness to concentrate on specific areas of evidence and enlarge upon what has already been said. The interviewer will focus the witness' attention to the relevant topic and probe each objective in turn to extract greater detail. Ideally open-ended question will be used to encourage a response but a mixture of open and closed questions may be necessary.

Fig 31

> ## Probing
>
> 'You say you left the house at 9.0pm? Tell me what you saw.'
> 'What lights did you leave on?'
> 'Who was at home when you left?'
> 'Who did you see?'
> 'Who left with you?'
> 'How often do you go out during the evening?'

The interviewer must identify to the witness the topic which is to be explored in greater depth and put a series of open-ended questions to draw information from him. The '*What? Where? When? Why? How? and Who?*' principles apply. As each objective is covered, the interviewer will move on to the next.

Fig 32

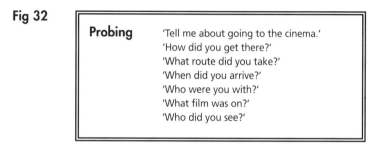

Probing   'Tell me about going to the cinema.'
'How did you get there?'
'What route did you take?'
'When did you arrive?'
'Who were you with?'
'What film was on?'
'Who did you see?'

These examples are for illustration purposes - obviously the interviewer will only probe those areas where more information is required. The interviewer fully probes each relevant parts of the witness' account before moving on to the next section of the interview.

Fig 33

Expanding the initial factual account

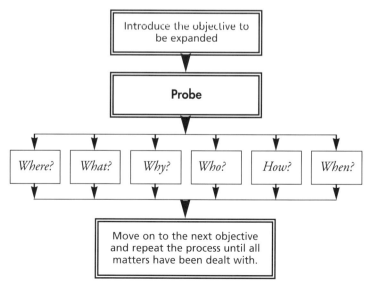

Introduce the objective to be expanded

Probe

Where?   What?   Why?   Who?   How?   When?

Move on to the next objective and repeat the process until all matters have been dealt with.

4. Dealing with the interviewer's objectives

The interviewer will have listed his objectives on the interview plan prior to commencing the interview and will have added to this list as the interview progressed. It is likely that most of these matters will have been mentioned by the witness in the course of his initial account and then explored as the account was probed in more detail. However the interviewer will now need to check the interview plan to in case there are any matters which may have been overlooked or simply not mentioned by the witness.

Matters not already dealt with in the witness' account can be regarded as the interviewer's objectives. Each objective in turn is presented to the witness and by use of an open-ended question the witness is asked his knowledge of it.

Fig 34

> ### Examples
>
> 'Some witnesses have referred to a van being at the scene. Do you know anything about a van?'
> 'Describe to me your involvement with the business accounts.'
> 'You told me an antique painting was stolen from your house. Will you describe this to me fully including identifying features?'

The interviewer's objectives may also include seeming inconsistencies or apparent lies. We have already said that these should be left to a late stage of the interview - it is now the time for potentially contentious issues to be put to the witness and fully probed in the same way as any other objectives.

Fig 35

> ### Clarification of inconsistencies
>
> 'You said you were alone when you saw the robbery occur. The lady who was robbed describes you being there, but says you were with a young woman. How do you account for that?'
>
> 'You say you got a good view of the robber as he ran under the street light but officers who were called to the scene say the street lights in the area were not working. What do you have to say about that?'

Fig 36

Dealing with the interviewer's objectives

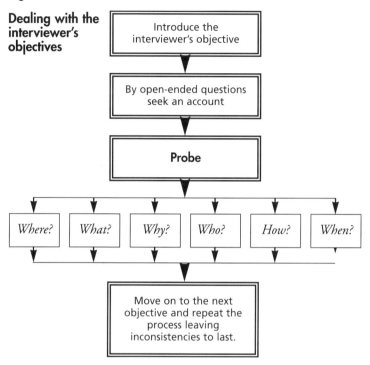

5. Review

It is now necessary to conclude the interview by reviewing what has been said. This is accomplished by summarising back to the witness all that has been said to check for accuracy and correct interpretation. This process applies regardless of the strategy used to expand the witness' account.

The review confirms that the necessary information has been obtained and it has been understood correctly by the interviewer. It allows the witness to correct any mistakes or misinterpretations.

The notes taken will assist the interviewer in reviewing the information and relating it back to the interviewee. A further advantage of summarising the account back to the witness is that it helps store the information in the interviewer's memory.

Fig 37

Review of a witness' account

'What you have said is that - you were standing alone in Millbank at 9.30pm last Thursday waiting for a taxi when you saw a lady about 60 years of age standing on the other side of the road. A man ran up to the woman from the direction of the bus station and snatched the woman's bag. He then ran off toward the Town Hall. You have not seen the man previously but describe him as 23 years of age, 5' 8", long fair hair and wearing dark clothing. The only words he said were 'Leave loose of your bag'. You got a good look at him, particularly as he passed the light of the street lamp, and you would recognise him if you were to see him again. Is that correct?'

A verbal summary may well result in more information being remembered and such matters should be dealt with in the same way as any other new information.

As soon as all relevant matters have been dealt with the interview should be concluded as no useful purpose will be served by repetitive and aimless questioning. Indeed it is likely to confuse witnesses or encourage some witnesses to add information to please the interviewer.

Witness' statement

An interview with a witness will normally be followed by taking down a witness statement. The interviewer will have completed the interview by summarising what has been said by reference to his notes which have now become the basis upon which to formulate a written statement.

Witness statements are required for a variety of purposes but the main reasons can be summarised as follows:

- to assist the police in determining the right action to be taken - for example, court proceedings, caution, no further action;
- to provide the Crown Prosecution Service with the evidence a witness can give in relation to an offence;
- to assist a prosecuting lawyer in the preparation of a case for court and assist in the examination of the witness;
- to make a formal record of information from a witness as to what occurred in an incident or during the commission of an offence;
- to provide the information for a coroner's court or other tribunal; for example, the Criminal Injuries Compensation Board.

The quality of witness statements and the evidence contained within them is vital to the prosecution case and ultimately reflects the level of professionalism of the officer preparing a file. Incident rooms for serious crime investigation rely heavily on high quality witness statements. These will often determine the direction of an investigation and ultimately the difference between success and failure.

The person reading the statement will often have no other knowledge of the incident, the individuals concerned, or the area in which it occurred. They therefore rely heavily upon the interviewing officer taking a detailed and unbiased statement providing them with as much reliable factual information as possible.

The statement should:
- be expressed in the first person;
- be in clear straightforward narrative form;
- follow the chronological sequence of the events or matters;
- as far as possible be in the language of the person making it.

The written statement must contain only such material facts as the witness is able to give from his own knowledge. It is the equivalent of the oral evidence the witness can provide at court and in some cases it may be served upon the court and accepted as such.

Summary

Time invested in conducting well-structured and factual interviews in the proper surroundings is time well spent. Obtaining and recording witness evidence is a crucial aspect of investigation, requiring a high degree of skill, and the importance of this task should not be under-estimated. The interviewer who fails to ask the appropriate questions, or fails to listen intently and objectively to what the witness is saying, has no long term future as an investigator.

The interviewing of witnesses should never be considered a routine task as the skills are at the very core of successful investigation. Interviews should take place in the best possible environment and be properly structured. An explanation of the procedures to be adopted, reasons for the interview, and the possible consequences of providing information to the police should be frankly but realistically presented to the witness. Any statement that is obtained should accurately reflect the witness' evidence and contain all the evidence available.

Witness evidence is crucial to a successful investigation and the standard of evidence achieved depends very much upon the skill, patience and attitude of the investigator.

CHAPTER 6

INTERVIEWING SUSPECTS

Introduction

Some researchers consider there is no difference between the style of interview required for a witness and that required for a suspect. We agree that there are many similarities, particularly in relation to structure, but an interview with a suspect is usually conducted in an entirely different atmosphere and within a vastly different legal framework. For this reason we have separated the two, and although some topics include in this chapter have already been introduced it is useful to consider them again specifically in relation to interviewing suspects.

The success or otherwise of an interview should not be measured by proof of a suspect's guilt. It is equally important, if not more so, to prove that a suspect was not involved in a crime and the sooner this can be established the sooner the police can concentrate their efforts upon identifying the person who is responsible. The purpose of an interview with a suspect is no different to that with a witness - to ascertain the truth of the matter under investigation

Interviewers must always enter an interview with an open mind and remain open-minded throughout the interview. At the same time they must not accept the account at face value but listen carefully and objectively to what is said. This must then be compared with what is already known, then probed at the appropriate time to help determine the truth and accuracy. Interviewers should be constantly aware of the adage - 'a man listens to what he wants to hear and disregards the rest'. A good interviewer listens to all that is said - disregarding information only when he is satisfied it is irrelevant but still keeping it in the back of his mind in case it later becomes relevant.

Pre-interview considerations

Before starting an interview a police officer must carry out as much preparatory work as he can although the amount of preparation possible will vary depending on the overall circumstances. Whether an interview succeeds or not will often be determined by the level of thought and preparation applied before the interview starts.

In ideal circumstances the interviewer will have been able to investigate fully the suspect's alleged involvement in the offence before he was arrested, and then thoroughly prepare and plan the interview before it starts. Unfortunately the nature of police work is such that many investigations are carried out in less than ideal circumstances but, to become effective investigators, police officers must do their best to follow good pre-interview practice. The essence is to investigate then interview - not interview then investigate.

Preparation and planning

The time available for preparation and planning will vary but interviewers should consider the following as the minimum necessary to allow the interviewer to competently conduct an interview.

Knowledge of the suspect
▌ Find out personal details including family circumstances, employment, and associates.
▌ Check previous convictions and crime intelligence.
▌ If possible speak to officers who have dealt with the suspect in the past.

Knowledge of the offence
▌ Visit the scene.
▌ Read available statements.
▌ Speak to witnesses including colleagues who have attended the scene or had contact with the suspect.
▌ Be aware of the geographical area in which the offence was committed.
▌ Determine whether the offence is isolated or one of a series.

Preparing an interview plan
The interview plan is a written agenda of items to be covered during the interview, presented in the form of objectives. These objectives will include all factual, legal and procedural matters which need to be addressed.

A change in the direction of the interview may be necessary and the interviewer should record in the plan his advance considerations of the options that could apply and the courses to take. This will particularly include what evidence should be disclosed to the suspect before and during the interview.

The right of silence has not been abolished and there will be some occasions when a suspect exercises his entitlement to not answer some or all of the questions put to him. Interviewers must also consider this as a possibility and prepare their reaction to it. They should be ready to adopt a strategy so that proper inference may be drawn by a court as to the suspect's failure or refusal to answer questions.

Determining the role of the interviewers

Discuss who is to be the main and secondary interviewer, and who is to keep notes of the interview. It is important that each interviewer understands their role and it is vital that they discipline themselves to conform with the agreed role. Two interviewers firing question after question in an unstructured manner are unlikely to achieve their objectives.

Administrative arrangements

Make sure adequate facilities are available for the interview including an interview room and any equipment or materials that may be required during the interview. Make sure all persons required to attend are available and aware of their responsibilities.

Disclosure

There is little point in conducting an interview with a suspect if he does not know why he is being interviewed. Not only would this be unfair on the suspect, but the interviewer would be unlikely to achieve the aim of his interview by asking a person to account for something and leaving him ignorant of what he is accounting for.

A solicitor representing a suspect has a duty to ensure his client is properly advised before the interview commences and, in order to fulfil this duty, the solicitor must be provided with some details concerning the offence alleged and the grounds upon which his client was arrested. If the solicitor is not given this information by the police prior to the interview he is likely to advise his client not to answer questions. A court may draw inference from a defendant's failure or refusal to answer questions during interview, but not if it believes the failure or refusal was reasonable.

It is therefore in the interests of all parties concerned for some information to be disclosed to the suspect and his solicitor before or at the beginning of the interview. An important aspect of planning an interview is to carefully consider what evidence should be disclosed to the suspect and his solicitor, and at what stage of the interview it should be disclosed. To disclose insufficient information could be unreasonable and result in evidence being excluded by the court, but to disclose too much information may harm an investigation.

Consider a situation in a case of rape in which DNA evidence is available linking a suspect with the offence. If the guilty suspect is aware of this evidence prior to the interview it is possible for him to falsely claim he had sexual intercourse with the victim with her consent. The same suspect, if not told the DNA evidence exists, may choose to deny sexual intercourse ever took place. Evidence of lies told by a suspect during an interview are not necessarily proof of guilt, but a court is entitled to take them into account along with other evidence in determining guilt or innocence. Another example may be where fingerprints are found inside premises following a burglary. A guilty suspect with knowledge of this may be tempted to state falsely that he had previously entered the premises lawfully.

Innocent suspects have nothing to fear from non-disclosure of all of the police evidence, provided they are fully aware of what is alleged against them. Indeed there will be occasions when it is to the advantage of the innocent person to be allowed to provide a full and uncontaminated account without knowledge of some of the evidence. Their innocence may become clear to the investigators at an earlier stage of the investigation. Equally, guilty suspects may wish to give a full, honest and uncontaminated account of what occurred, but they should not be given the opportunity to fabricate a defence or an alibi around the police evidence.

Some solicitors may argue they are entitled to know of all the police evidence before the interview starts so that they may properly advise their clients, but there is no legal foundation for this claim. There is no statutory right for solicitors to be given full verbal disclosure, copies of witness statements, or other documents at this stage of an investigation. A solicitor who has full knowledge of the police evidence would be obliged to disclose it to the suspect during private consultation prior to the interview starting. The only legal requirements upon the police to disclose information are that the suspect and his solicitor must be told the nature of the offence of which he is suspected. They must be told the grounds for the suspect's arrest and the solicitor may examine the custody record in relation to anything that must be recorded upon it by law. The solicitor is not entitled to a copy of the custody record until after the suspect has left custody.

On no account should the interviewer attempt to mislead the suspect or his solicitor (for example, falsely denying that fingerprint evidence is available, or implying that it may be when it is not) because this would this be unfair to the suspect and highly likely to be deemed unlawful. Evidence gained by such deception will surely be ruled inadmissible by the court.

Consideration of what evidence should be disclosed is a matter for the investigating officer. In most cases the investigating officer will also be the interviewer, but in serious crime inquiries it may be a senior investigating officer who has responsibility for managing interviews carried out by others. In such cases there is merit in the senior investigating officer appointing an officer to deal specifically with the matter of disclosure. This officer, in consultation with the senior investigating officer, the interviewing officer, and other appropriate members of of the incident management team, will formally disclose evidence to the suspect's solicitor at the beginning of the interview, and at other stages of the interview as considered appropriate. This may minimise conflict between the interviewers and the solicitor and allow them to concentrate upon the incident itself.

A custody officer has an impartial role and cannot be expected to know of all the evidence. Any requests by solicitors to custody officers for detailed information about evidence should be referred to investigating officers, and on no account should custody officers become involved in such discussions with solicitors.

During the planning stage the investigating officer must consider:
■ what evidence is to be disclosed prior to the interview;
■ in the event of some evidence being withheld, at what stage of the interview it should be disclosed.

It will usually be the case that the interviewer will prefer to hear what the suspect has to say about the allegation before he gives detailed disclosure of the evidence. He will often outline to the suspect the offence alleged; ask a suspect to account for his movements at the time of the offence, and then disclose later in the interview any incriminating evidence, including fingerprint or DNA identification or independent eye witness accounts.

Fig 38

> **Example**
>
> 'As you are aware, you have been arrested for a house burglary which occurred between 1.30pm and 4.15pm yesterday afternoon at 12 West Road when a large quantity of antiques were stolen. Can you tell me about your movements yesterday?'

There will be occasions when it is tactical to disclose all of the evidence at the beginning of the interview.

Fig 39

> **Example:**
>
> 'As you are aware you have been arrested for shoplifting earlier today. You were seen by the store detective to pick up articles from the shop display and then walk out without paying. When the store detective approached you outside the shop you ran off discarding the stolen goods in the street. When the store detective caught up with you, you said: "I'm sorry I stole them but I could not afford to pay for them." Tell me in your own words your account of what happened.'

There will also be occasions when the interviewer does not disclose some parts of the evidence at any stage of the interview as he considers it to be tactically beneficial to carry out further investigations following the interview before the suspect learns of the evidence. The evidence may be disclosed in a subsequent interview or not disclosed in any interview at all.

An officer must adopt a professional and tactical approach to pre-interview disclosure in all investigations. The tactics used should be those that best suit the individual investigation having regard to all the circumstances. Officers should be mindful that a court may not be able to draw inference from a person's silence or failure to answer questions if the suspect is not given the opportunity to comment upon the evidence concerned. Furthermore in most circumstances the evidence will eventually be disclosed before the court proceedings in the form of pre-trial advance disclosure.

Solicitors will usually ask if all the evidence has been disclosed and on some occasions may ask if specific evidence exists. It is not uncommon for a solicitor to ask these questions as soon as the tape recorder has been switched on. The interviewer's response should be to quote the following:

> *'I have provided you with what I consider to be the fullest appropriate information and now intend to interview your client and ask him to provide an account of the incident.'*

There is also merit in the officer repeating exactly what has been disclosed to the suspect and his solicitor, particularly if this is on tape, so there can be no dispute over it at a later stage. For this purpose the officer should write down the information that is to be disclosed when planning the interview. The note can be referred to on tape and retained in case it is required in court.

A suspect is still entitled to exercise his right of silence and it is for the solicitor to advise him what he considers best in the circumstances. It is for the solicitor to balance the advantages and disadvantages of refusal or failure to answer questions and act in the best interests of his client. The interviewer should be prepared to deal with such a response and to proceed with the interview in accordance with the interview plan. As new evidence is released the solicitor may wish to review his advice and seek a break in the interview for private consultation. The interviewer should not respond to a failure or refusal to answer questions by immediately disclosing all the evidence, but by repeating on tape the salient points of what is alleged, giving the suspect the opportunity to comment. It is not necessary to disclose all evidence provided the interviewer considers the consequences of non-disclosure in relation to inferences that can be drawn from silence. Particular consideration should be given to special warnings *(see following section)*.

There may be some officers who consider total disclosure to be the easy option and usually disclose all of the evidence - except on those occasions when fingerprint or similar incriminating evidence is available. These officers should not be surprised when the solicitor, who is familiar with the officers' usual attitude toward disclosure, advises the suspect to say nothing because he suspects information is being withheld. A consistent, professional and tactical approach should be adopted in all cases, not just in those cases where it is believed necessary to withhold information.

Police officers should understand the right of a suspect to remain silent, and also the enthusiasm of defence lawyers to be allowed disclosure of all evidence before the suspect gives his account. Law Society guidelines strongly urge solicitors to seek full disclosure prior to an interview but, as we have said, these are not legally binding. The solicitor has a duty to represent a client in his best possible interests and full knowledge of the police case would assist him in deciding the best course of action he should take.

> *The police responsibility is much wider than that of the defence lawyer because, in addition to a legal and moral duty to be scrupulously fair to suspects, they have the added responsibility of fairly representing the interests of victim of crime and society generally. To invite a guilty suspect to fabricate a defence around the police evidence would not serve those wider interests.*

Conducting the interview - five stages of interview

The interview should be structured into five identifiable areas. These differ from the five stages of the witness interview discussed in the previous chapter, as the emphasis here is to check the accuracy of the account, examine apparent inconsistencies and allow for potential conflict. Also, legal procedures must be considered.

1. Starting the interview - legal and procedural matters.
2. Obtaining the suspect's account of the matter under investigation.
3. Dealing with the interviewer's objectives.
4. Confrontation - challenging lies and inconsistencies.
5. Closing the interview.

It is imperative that the interviewer recognises each individual stage of the interview so that it may progress in a controlled and structured manner. These stages also provide convenient areas where the interviewer may break the interview if necessary. A break in the interview may be to allow the interviewer to reappraise the interview objectives, to conduct further investigations, or simply for both parties to refresh themselves if the interview is lengthy or complex. Interviewers may consider a break at the completion of any stage of the interview rather than to continue regardless of new issues that may arise. Time constraints must be considered but breaks do not have to be for a long period of time, as some issues can be resolved by a telephone call or brief conversation with a witness or colleague.

Fig 40

The five stages of the suspect interview

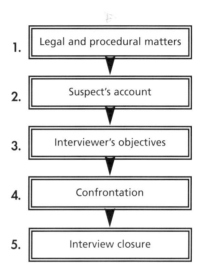

1. Legal and procedural matters
2. Suspect's account
3. Interviewer's objectives
4. Confrontation
5. Interview closure

1. Starting the interview - legal and procedural matters

Tape recording procedures
Interviews with suspects must be tape recorded in the following cases:
- an interview under caution with a person who is suspected of committing an indictable offence (including those triable either way);
- when a police officer puts further questions to a suspect about an indictable offence as above, after the suspect has been charged with the offence or informed that they may be prosecuted for it;
- any interview in which a police officer wishes to bring to the notice of a person, after they have been charged or informed that they may be prosecuted for the offence, any written statement made by another person or the content of an interview with another person - this includes playing back the tape recording of an accomplice.

There is no reason why interviewers should not record other types of interview on tape although individual forces may have policy on this. Examples of when recording may be beneficial include certain summary offences such as driving while disqualified, fatal road accidents or other complex road traffic cases. The advantages of tape recording outweigh the disadvantages, and common sense should dictate when tape recording is possible and to the advantage of all parties involved.

Any tape recorded interview should be recorded openly and in accordance with the Codes of Practice. The tape recording should start without delay and it is advisable for officers to adhere rigidly to this. An inordinate amount of time between a suspect being transferred from the custody officer and the recording starting could leave the interviewer vulnerable to allegations of off-tape impropriety. Officers should be able to account for this time and ensure it is recorded on the custody record.

The tapes must be unwrapped in the presence of the suspect and inserted in the tape recorder. The suspect must be formally told by the interviewing officer about the tape recording. The officer must say that the interview is being tape recorded, state his name and rank and that of any other officer present. He must give the name of the suspect and the name of any other persons present, for example a solicitor or appropriate adult. The date, time and place of the interview must be announced and it must be stated that the suspect will be given a written notice about what will happen to the tape. Though not compulsory it is good practice for the interviewing officer to ask each person present to identify themselves on tape for voice identification purposes.

The caution

Having completed these introductory formalities the suspect must be cautioned in the following terms:

> *'You do not have to say anything. But it may harm your defence if you do not mention when questioned something which you later rely on in court. Anything you say may be given in evidence.'*

Minor deviations from the caution are permissible provided the sense is preserved but professional police officers should memorise it. If there are any doubts surrounding the suspect's understanding of the caution the interviewer should explain the caution in simple terms. It is the interviewer's responsibility to ensure the suspect fully understands the caution and one way of checking a suspect's understanding is to ask the suspect to explain what it means.

Entitlement to legal advice

Once the interviewee has been cautioned, he must be reminded by the interviewing officer of his right to free and independent legal advice and that he can speak to a solicitor on the telephone if he so wishes.

Significant statements or silence

After the suspect has been reminded of his right to legal advice, the interviewing officer must put to him any significant statement or relevant comments made before the start of the tape recorded interview. Similarly, the suspect's silence, that is, any failure or refusal to answer a question or to answer it satisfactorily, must be put to him. The suspect should then be asked by the interviewing officer whether he confirms or denies the significant statement or silence made earlier, and whether he wishes to add anything.

While the significant statement or silence must be put to the suspect at the beginning of the interview, it is not necessary for the interviewer to continue questioning the suspect about it at that stage. It may be a convenient time to explore what has been said but, if the comments are likely to be confrontational or relate to a sensitive topic, early probing may lead to a conflict situation which inhibits further communication. It may be more effective for matters likely to cause conflict to be left to the later stages of the interview. Consideration should be given to this prior to the start of the interview and included as part of the interview plan.

Special warnings

In some circumstances when a suspect is interviewed after arrest and fails or refuses to answer certain questions or to answer them satisfactorily after due warning, a court or jury may draw proper inference from that silence.

For an inference to be drawn from the suspect's failure or refusal to answer a question about one of these matters, or to answer it satisfactorily, the interviewing officer must first tell the suspect in ordinary language:

▌ what offence is being investigated;
▌ what fact the suspect is being asked to account for;
▌ that it is believed this fact may be due to the suspect taking part in the commission of the offence in question;
▌ that a court may draw a proper inference from his silence if the suspect fails or refuses to account for the fact about which he is being questioned;
▌ that a record is being made of the interview and may be given in evidence if the suspect is brought to trial.

The legislation states that, for any proper inferences to be drawn, a warning must be given during the interview. It does not stipulate at which point of the interview this should be, leaving it to the discretion of the individual officer. In most cases it may be appropriate to give the warning at the beginning of the interview. However, the interviewer may feel on some occasions that this is likely to provoke conflict with the suspect and is therefore inappropriate at this stage. The interviewer may prefer to start the interview by inviting the suspect to give his account of the matter, leaving the special warning to later, possibly the challenge stage of the interview. The interviewer should make this decision during the planning stage and it should be included in the written interview plan.

Introducing exhibits

It may be necessary to introduce exhibits during the interview and this also requires advance consideration. In some cases it may be possible to have exhibits at hand during the interview but on other occasions a more discreet approach may be necessary and they may have to be brought in from outside the interview room either while the tape is still running or after a short break.

Fig 41

Starting the interview

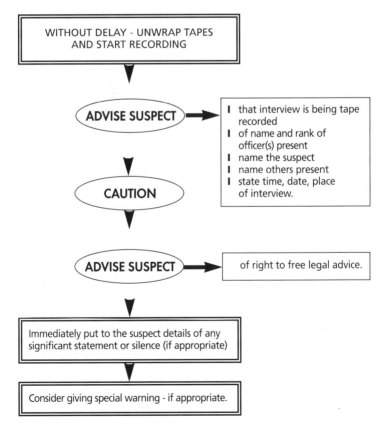

Once these formalities have been completed, the interviewer has an opportunity to explain to the suspect the reasons for the interview and the procedures to be followed. The procedures include the role of the interviewers, the structure of the interview, and the reason for note taking.

Once this has been done the factual interview can start in earnest.

2. Obtaining an account from the suspect

The interviewer should begin the interview by allowing the suspect to give his own account of the facts surrounding the matter under investigation, remembering that the wording of the first question is of paramount importance.

The interviewer should allow the suspect to give the account in his own words and at his own pace. While the suspect is giving the account the interviewer should not interrupt the flow of conversation but allow him to complete what he wishes to say.

In the ideal situation the interviewer will receive a comprehensive and detailed account of the suspect's knowledge of the matter under investigation. However, the extent of the account will vary from suspect to suspect, depending on knowledge of the incident, personality, communication skills and the degree to which the suspect is prepared to provide information.

Suspects should be allowed to give their account from whatever starting point they choose, but in some cases it may be useful for the interviewer to give an indication of the desired starting and finishing point so that the suspect fully understands what is required.

Fig 42

Typical opening questions

Q 'Tell me about your movements from first leaving your home yesterday morning and then returning home last night.'

Q 'Tell me what happened last Thursday from when you first entered the Black Horse public house until you left.'

Q 'Tell me what your involvement is with the offence.'

An interviewer should only define parameters when absolutely certain of the times and dates the offence occurred. To define parameters when unsure of exactly when the offence occurred could result in the interviewee providing misleading or incomplete information. If in doubt either do not stipulate parameters or make them sufficiently wide to encourage the suspect to give the fullest possible account.

It is advisable to start off much earlier than the offence could have possibly been committed, taking into account preparatory acts or meeting up with accomplices. Also consider that it is often better for the suspect to start off in a non-contentious area rather than to immediately talk about the offence. Non-contentious matters are easier to talk about and this allows the suspect to become used to talking to the interviewer, gradually moving toward the contentious area.

A common feature of interviews is for the person being interviewed not to answer the opening question, but to respond with whatever is uppermost in their mind at the time of the interview.

Fig 43

Typical response to opening question

Q 'Tell me what happened last Thursday when you were in the Black Horse public house.'

   R 'I don't even know why I have been arrested, I've done nothing wrong.'

Faced with such a response interviewers commonly react by reverting to closed questions rather than persisting with questions worded to encourage an extended response. The result is a series of closed questions from which little information is gained. Questioning becomes repetitive and the interviewer loses control of the interview. Little is achieved and it becomes increasingly unlikely the correct structure will ever be regained.

Fig 44

Typical response from interviewer when interviewee does not answer opening question

Q 'Tell me what happened last Thursday when you were in the Black Horse public house?'

cont overleaf…

> **Q** *cont from previous page...*
> **R**   'I don't even know why I have
>   been arrested, I've done nothing wrong.'
> **Q** Did you go into the Black Horse public house last Thursday?'
> **R**   'Yes.'
> **Q** 'What time did you go in?'
> **R**   'Half past seven.'
> **Q** 'Were there many people in the pub when you went in?'
> **R**   'Yes.'

For suspects to initially respond with their own concerns rather than to your questions is very common and interviewers should always, as part of the interview plan, have a second open-ended question in reserve to deal with the situation. A good tactic may be for the interviewer to briefly respond to the suspect's concerns and then resume with an open-ended question seeking the suspect's account.

Fig 45

> ### Tactic for dealing with suspect who is avoiding the question
>
> **Q** 'Tell me what happened last Thursday evening when you were in the
>   Black Horse public house?'
> **R**   'I don't even know why I have been arrested, I've done nothing
>   wrong.'
> **Q** 'The reason for your arrest has been fully explained to you. I am now
>   giving you the opportunity to give your account of what happened.
>   Tell me what happened last Thursday evening when you were in the
>   Black Horse public house.'

Repetition of the open-ended question usually has the desired effect of encouraging the suspect to respond with a relevant and more detailed answer and the interviewer keeps control of the interview. Should the second question meet with a further inadequate response the interviewer may have to deal in more depth with whatever is on the suspect's mind before returning to seek an account using another open-ended question.

Another common response is for suspects, guilty or not, to respond simply by saying they know nothing about the offence. On receiving this response the interviewer should be prepared to change tactics by asking the suspect to account for his movements at the relevant time rather than his knowledge of the offence.

Fig 46

A flexible approach

Q 'A burglary took place yesterday afternoon at Forum Way. Tell me
what you know about it.'

   R 'I know nothing about it.'

Q 'Tell me your movements from when you first got out of bed
yesterday morning.'

An open-ended question such as this will normally encourage an extended
account of the suspect's movement at the time of the offence. The movements
can be investigated and, in the case of a guilty suspect, some discrepancy may
be found.

A common fault among interviewers is to interrupt the suspect before he has
been allowed to give a full account. Often this is because the suspect appears
to tell a lie or is inconsistent in some respect. It is very tempting for an interviewer to immediately challenge the suspect who tells a blatant lie, particularly when there is evidence to contradict it. However, to challenge at an early
stage may allow the dishonest suspect to re-adjust his account in accordance
with the evidence.

Allowing the suspect to continue telling lies and even to compound the lies
during the probing stage can be to a useful strategy. The tape recorder should
be used in such circumstances to the interviewer's advantage.

It is also possible that the suspect is being truthful, but is mistaken. Should
the interviewer immediately challenge the misconception a compliant suspect
may feel inclined to change the account to please the interviewer. As the interview progresses the suspect may then be forced to tell lies to support this. In
these circumstances a miscarriage of justice could ensue. The tactic of allowing
the interviewee to continue with the account unchallenged may result in the
mistake being rectified and it becoming clear to the interviewer that a mistake
had been made. If this is not the case the probing of the account is likely to clarify the situation.

Interruptions, whether they be intended to correct an inconsistency, challenge
a lie, or simply ask a question, do not contribute to good interviewing as they
inhibit the flow of information.

On occasions when more than one interviewer is to be involved, the interviewers will need to decide at the planning stage the role of each interviewer and

in particular who is to be the main interviewer and who is to make the notes. Some interviewers prefer to each maintain their respective notes to eliminate any difficulty in interpretation. In any event the key topics and issues disclosed by the interviewee should be noted for later reference using a key word to prompt the interviewer's recollection.

Once it appears the suspect has given all the information he is likely to the interviewer should, by reference to the notes, verbally summarise back to the suspect what has been said. The purpose of this is to check for accuracy of interpretation and to allow the suspect to correct any mistakes that may have been made.

In the ideal situation the account given would be a detailed and complete account which requires no further explanation but this is highly unlikely and the interviewer must now probe the account to expand it and to check for inconsistencies.

Probing the suspect's account

The interviewer's notes will have divided the account into key topics. At the end of the initial account the interviewer should quickly review the notes to identify the topics requiring clarification or expansion. For illustration purposes the following shows a very brief account given by a suspect, and the type of notes which may have been maintained by the interviewer.

Fig 47

Noting key topics

Q 'Tell me about your movements last night?'
  R 'I left the house, went to the pub, played darts and then went back home'

NOTES:

    LEFT HOUSE
    WENT TO PUB
    DARTS
    RETURNED HOME

Each topic or issue identified should be considered as an objective for further investigation and identified on the notes.

Fig 48

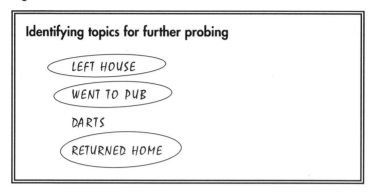

Identifying topics for further probing

- LEFT HOUSE
- WENT TO PUB
- DARTS
- RETURNED HOME

The above example, for illustration purposes only, shows that the fact that the suspect played darts does not require probing. The interviewer continues by putting a series of questions to the suspect in respect of each of the topics identified. The aim is to expand each topic to gain maximum information and to check for accuracy and truthfulness.

Fig 49

Expanding the account

Left house
'Where do you live?'
'What time did you leave home?'
'Who was at home when you left?'
'Who saw you leave?'

Went to pub
'Which pub did you go to?'
'How did you get there?'
'Why did you go to that particular pub?'
'Who was in the pub when you got there?'
'Where in the pub were you standing?'
'Who saw you there?'

Returned home
'What time did you leave the pub?'
'Who did you leave with?'
'What route did you take?'
'Who did you see?'
'What time did you return home?'

Interviewers should remember that open-ended questions result in more information and should be used whenever possible even in the probing stage. Closed questions will be necessary to obtain direct information but a mix of open and closed questions may be desirable, particularly with articulate or talkative suspects.

Fig 50

Using mixed questions

'What time did you leave the house?'
'Tell me about your journey to the public house.'
'Tell me what you did in the public house.'
'Who else was there?'
'What time did you leave?'
'Tell me about your journey home.'

Each objective in turn is probed by the interviewer before moving on to the next. Any apparent lies or inconsistencies should not be challenged at this stage but noted for examination later in the interview.

When the interviewer has probed all the objectives relating to the suspect's account he should ask the second interviewer, if appropriate, if there are any matters he wishes to clarify. The second interviewer's role is to 'sweep up' any points which may have been overlooked or not adequately probed and it is important that aspects outside the parameters of what has already been said (that is, the suspect's account) are not mentioned. In complex or lengthy interviews there may be merit in more regular planned interventions by the second interviewer. A strict discipline needs to be maintained between interviewers and each must abide by their respective role.

Once the second interviewer has completed to his satisfaction he should pass back to the main interviewer who should, by reference to his notes, verbally summarise back to the suspect what has been said checking for correct interpretation and accuracy. Once this has been completed the interviewer should have full knowledge of what the interviewee is prepared to impart about his movements or activities in relation to the alleged offence.

The interviewer will have given no indication as to whether the account is consistent or not with the other evidence. The task was to obtain the fullest possible account from the suspect and to probe it testing for accuracy and truthfulness.

Fig 51

Obtaining the suspect' account

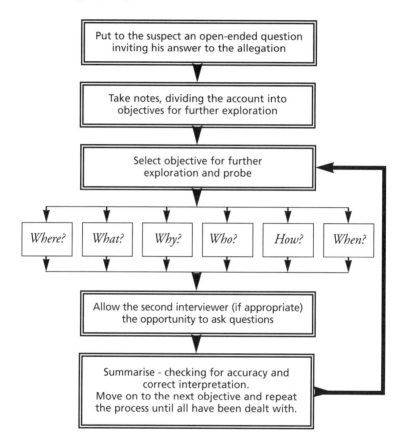

The interviewer now needs to move on to the next stage of the interview and deal with the objectives which are contained in the interview plan and which have not already been mentioned in the suspect's account.

3. Dealing with the interviewer's objectives

The interviewer has dealt with the suspect's account by dividing it into topics, so that the key aspects may be identified as objectives to be examined in greater depth.

However, it is unlikely that the suspect will have covered all the objectives originally formulated in the interview plan, or indeed that the interviewer may have added to his plan as the interview progressed.

It may be that the suspect has deliberately avoided issues, overlooked them, or not appreciated their relevance. The interviewer now needs to deal with remaining objectives listed on the plan.

Each interviewer's objective should be dealt with in an identical way to objectives covered within the suspect's account. The interviewer, by use of open-ended questions, introduces each objective separately and seeks an account of it. The suspect should be allowed to answer in his own time and in his own words. The interviewer should not interrupt and should not at this stage challenge any apparent lies or inconsistencies.

Each objective should be fully probed and the second interviewer, if appropriate, invited to ask questions to clarify or pick up on any missed points.

The main interviewer then verbally summarises the objective to check interpretation and accuracy before moving on to the next. The process continues until each objective has been has been dealt with.

Any aspects likely to be contentious and which require what amounts to a challenge should be left to the next stage of the interview, rather than risk contaminating the account or creating conflict between the interviewer and suspect. If a breakdown in relationship between the suspect and interviewer is to develop it is better for it to happen as late as possible in the interview when all other objectives have been dealt with.

Challenges may include confronting the suspect with apparent lies or inconsistencies in his account.

Fig 52

Dealing with the interviewer's objectives

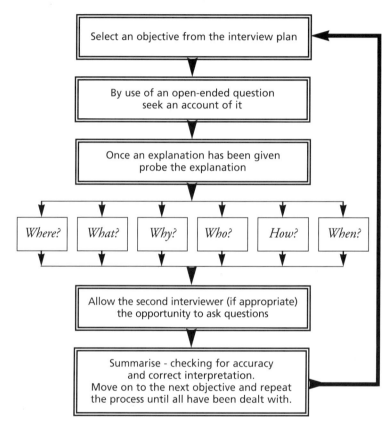

4. Confrontation

Saving contentious issues for a fourth stage of the interview is particularly important with suspect interviews. Despite the need to check the truth and accuracy of the account, reactions of anger or other tactics to avoid giving explanations are best avoided for as long as possible. Valuable information may otherwise be lost and the interviewer denied the opportunity to examine with the suspect important objectives rising from his account or from other available evidence.

A premature challenge could also confuse the innocent suspect whereas, if he were allowed to continue talking, he may clarify a inconsistency or rectify a mistake. Very nervous suspects or those with intellectual difficulties may be tempted to adjust their account to please the interviewer. Furthermore, an immediate challenge may allow a deceitful suspect to adjust his account to suit the evidence - there is more merit in allowing him to confirm and compound the lie.

The term 'challenge' should not be misunderstood. The challenge should be put to the suspect in the same manner as the questions earlier in the interview. There is no need for raised voices or offensive language. Not only is this a breach of the law but it may be counterproductive as it can contribute to a breakdown in the conversation providing the suspect with an excuse to avoid giving answers. The challenge should be put calmly and in clear terms allowing the suspect every opportunity to understand what is being suggested and to account for it.

The interviewer will have identified apparent lies or inconsistencies during earlier stages of the interview and recorded them in the interview notes. Each should be dealt with as an individual objective. The interviewer should introduce each objective in the form of an open-ended question and seek an account of it from the suspect.

Fig 53

Example

'During the course of this interview you have consistently denied ever being inside the shop at 12 West Street. How do you account for the fact that your fingerprints were found inside the premises immediately after the burglary?'

Once that objective has been completed the second interviewer can be allowed the opportunity to ask questions on any aspect relating to that topic which may have been overlooked by the main interviewer. The second interviewer then passes back to the main interviewer to introduce the next objective and the process is repeated until all objectives have been dealt with.

Alternatively the main interviewer can complete all objectives of the confrontation stage before allowing the second interviewer to 'sweep up', after which the second interviewer passes back to the main interviewer for closure.

In the event of a suspect changing his account entirely after being challenged, the interviewer should return to the first stage, seeking a full account from him and them progressing through each stage again.

Fig 54

Confrontation

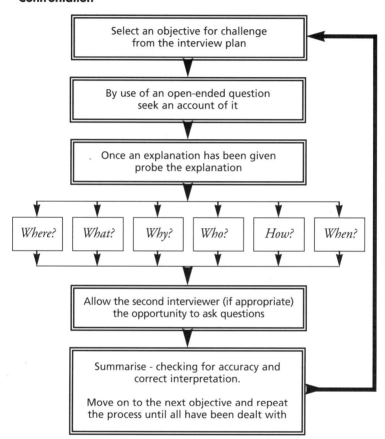

5. Closing the interview

Closure of the interview is not a simply a formality but a very important part of the interview procedure. The closure should not be delayed by repetitive questioning, going over matters again and again, but concluded as soon as all relevant matters have been dealt with. Not only does repetitive questioning achieve nothing other than create confusion but in some circumstances it may be deemed by the court to be oppressive.

Once all relevant matters have been dealt with the interview should be brought to a planned and structured closure. Abrupt endings should be avoided and sufficient time should be allowed for the completion of legal requirements and explanation of the next stages of the investigation.

The legal requirements in a tape recorded interview are as follows:
I   ask the suspect if there has anything he wishes to say;
I   give the suspect a copy of the notice explaining how he can get a copy of the tape;
I   state on tape the time at the end of the interview;
I   switch off the tape recorder;
I   ask the suspect to sign the completed master tape label and then seal the tape in his presence.

The next stage is to explain to the suspect what is to happen next and the reason for it. This may include informing him he will be:
I   released having been eliminated from inquiries;
I   bailed pending further inquiries;
I   charged with an offence and either detained or bailed to court;
I   detained pending further inquiries.

The interview may be one of a series or the interviewer may meet the suspect on a future occasion in relation to another matter. How the suspect feels on parting company with the interviewer will dictate the relationship on any future meeting. Interviewers should aim for long-term credibility with those they question, and the fair and proper treatment of a person suspected of offences can be an investment for the future.

Summary

Dividing the interview into five identifiable stages allows the interviewer to conduct an exhaustive interview in a manageable and controlled way, enabling him to probe in depth the account given and to explore any other relevant areas. It provides the suspect with every opportunity to give an uncontaminated account of his version of events.

It provides a 'language' between interviewers so that they can recognise each stage of the interview. A senior investigating officer can delegate interviewers to obtain a 'suspect's account' of what happened and then return to the incident room to discuss tactics before progressing further. The senior investigating officer then has the ability to confidently assign others to interview suspects while managing the interview from outside the interview room.

PART THREE

THE LAW

This book is intended as a guide to operational officers and the relevant legislation has been simplified and presented in an easy-to-read format that can be readily understood. This practical interpretation should not be regarded as a definitive work of reference and further research may be necessary to clarify finer points of the law.

CHAPTER 7

THE LAW - A PRACTICAL INTERPRETATION

When must a written record of interview be kept?

CODES OF PRACTICE - CODE C 11

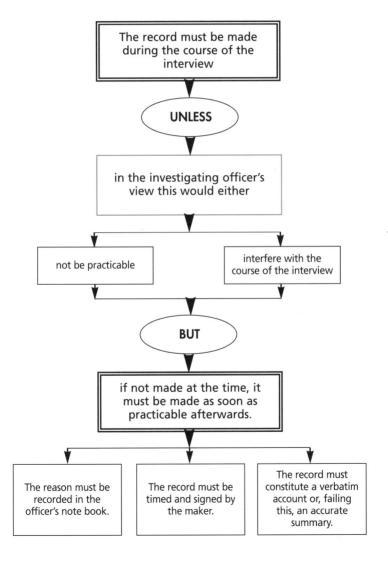

The record must be made during the course of the interview

UNLESS

in the investigating officer's view this would either

not be practicable

interfere with the course of the interview

BUT

if not made at the time, it must be made as soon as practicable afterwards.

The reason must be recorded in the officer's note book.

The record must be timed and signed by the maker.

The record must constitute a verbatim account or, failing this, an accurate summary.

What detail must be recorded within a written record of interview?

CODES OF PRACTICE - CODE C 11

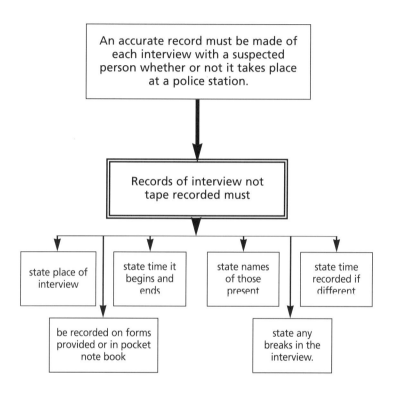

An accurate record must be made of each interview with a suspected person whether or not it takes place at a police station.

Records of interview not tape recorded must

state place of interview

state time it begins and ends

state names of those present

state time recorded if different

be recorded on forms provided or in pocket note book

state any breaks in the interview.

What is oppression?

POLICE AND CRIMINAL EVIDENCE ACT 1984 - SECTION 76

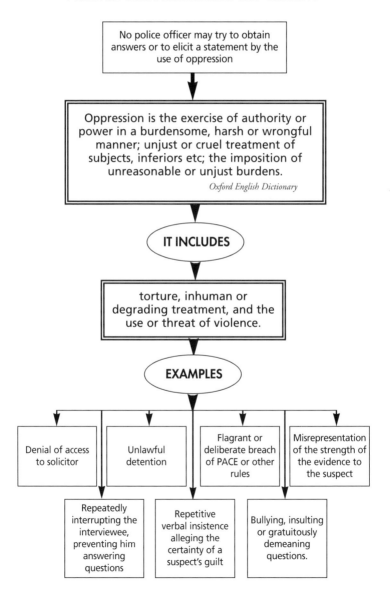

No police officer may try to obtain answers or to elicit a statement by the use of oppression

Oppression is the exercise of authority or power in a burdensome, harsh or wrongful manner; unjust or cruel treatment of subjects, inferiors etc; the imposition of unreasonable or unjust burdens.

Oxford English Dictionary

IT INCLUDES

torture, inhuman or degrading treatment, and the use or threat of violence.

EXAMPLES

Denial of access to solicitor

Unlawful detention

Flagrant or deliberate breach of PACE or other rules

Misrepresentation of the strength of the evidence to the suspect

Repeatedly interrupting the interviewee, preventing him answering questions

Repetitive verbal insistence alleging the certainty of a suspect's guilt

Bullying, insulting or gratuitously demeaning questions.

What action should be taken if a suspect asks what will happen if he answers questions, makes a statement, or refuses to do either?

CODES OF PRACTICE - CODE C 11

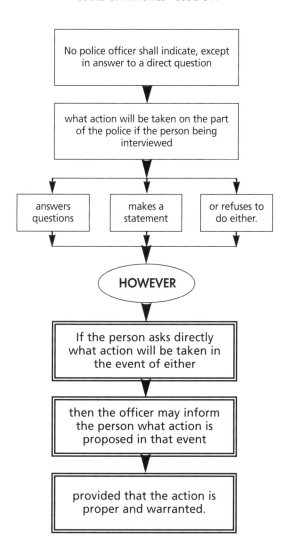

No police officer shall indicate, except in answer to a direct question

↓

what action will be taken on the part of the police if the person being interviewed

↓

answers questions | makes a statement | or refuses to do either.

↓

HOWEVER

↓

If the person asks directly what action will be taken in the event of either

↓

then the officer may inform the person what action is proposed in that event

↓

provided that the action is proper and warranted.

When must the interview with a suspect be stopped?

CODES OF PRACTICE - CODE C 11

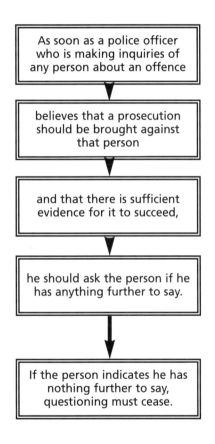

As soon as a police officer who is making inquiries of any person about an offence

believes that a prosecution should be brought against that person

and that there is sufficient evidence for it to succeed,

he should ask the person if he has anything further to say.

If the person indicates he has nothing further to say, questioning must cease.

What treatment should a person receive while being interviewed?

CODES OF PRACTICE - CODE C 12

In a period of 24 hours, a suspect must have eight hours of rest, free from questioning, preferably at night.

No one should be questioned while under the influence of drink or drugs.

In addition to meal breaks, there should be short breaks for refreshments every two hours unless it would prejudice the investigation.

Interview rooms must be adequately heated, lit and ventilated.

Suspects should not be required to stand.

Interviewers should identify themselves and their rank.

Can a period of rest be delayed?

CODES OF PRACTICE - CODE C 12

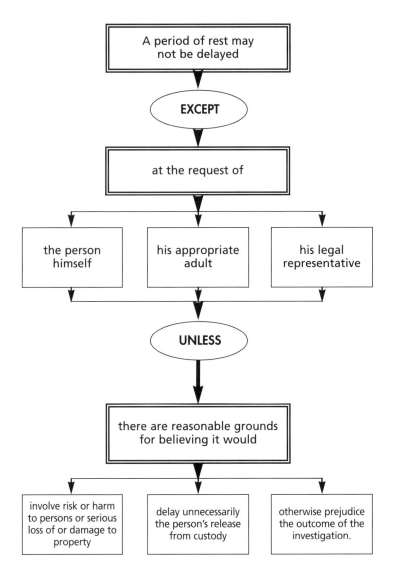

When should interviews be tape recorded?

CODES OF PRACTICE - CODE D

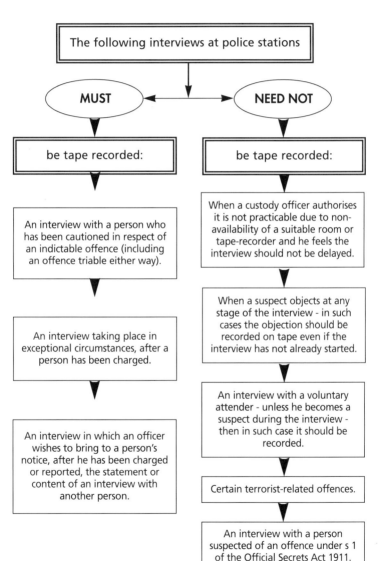

The following interviews at police stations

MUST ↔ **NEED NOT**

be tape recorded:

be tape recorded:

An interview with a person who has been cautioned in respect of an indictable offence (including an offence triable either way).

An interview taking place in exceptional circumstances, after a person has been charged.

An interview in which an officer wishes to bring to a person's notice, after he has been charged or reported, the statement or content of an interview with another person.

When a custody officer authorises it is not practicable due to non-availability of a suitable room or tape-recorder and he feels the interview should not be delayed.

When a suspect objects at any stage of the interview - in such cases the objection should be recorded on tape even if the interview has not already started.

An interview with a voluntary attender - unless he becomes a suspect during the interview - then in such case it should be recorded.

Certain terrorist-related offences.

An interview with a person suspected of an offence under s 1 of the Official Secrets Act 1911.

What is the caution?

CODES OF PRACTICE - CODE C 10

THE CAUTION

'You do not have to say anything. But it may harm your defence if you do not mention when questioned something which you later rely on in court. Anything you say may be given in evidence.'

The wording
Minor deviations do not constitute a breach provided the sense is preserved.

Understanding of caution
If a person appears not to understand what the caution means, the officer should repeat it in his own words.

Keeping a record
A record shall be made when a caution is given, either in the officer's note book or in the interview record.

Silence
Includes not only a failure or refusal to answer, but also a failure or refusal to answer a question satisfactorily.

Appropriate adult
When the presence of an appropriate adult is required and the suspect is cautioned outside their presence they should be cautioned again once the appropriate adult arrives.

Caution not necessary if
the questioning is solely to establish identity, vehicle ownership or in accordance with a statutory requirement, eg some traffic offences.

When must a person be cautioned?

CODES OF PRACTICE - CODE C 12

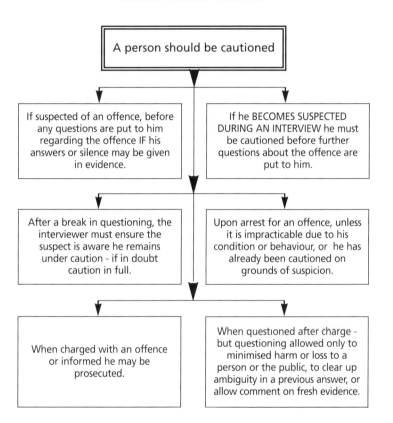

A person should be cautioned

If suspected of an offence, before any questions are put to him regarding the offence IF his answers or silence may be given in evidence.

If he BECOMES SUSPECTED DURING AN INTERVIEW he must be cautioned before further questions about the offence are put to him.

After a break in questioning, the interviewer must ensure the suspect is aware he remains under caution - if in doubt caution in full.

Upon arrest for an offence, unless it is impracticable due to his condition or behaviour, or he has already been cautioned on grounds of suspicion.

When charged with an offence or informed he may be prosecuted.

When questioned after charge - but questioning allowed only to minimised harm or loss to a person or the public, to clear up ambiguity in a previous answer, or allow comment on fresh evidence.

What if a suspect asks to make a written statement?

CODES OF PRACTICE - CODE C 12

The vast majority of interviews under caution will be tape recorded and, if not, contemporaneously recorded. It is therefore normally unnecessary for a a written statement to be taken except at the interviewee's express wish.

If it is necessary to take a written statement under caution, a person MUST BE INVITED to write down himself what he wants to say, though on some occasions the interviewee may ask the officer to write it for him.

WRITTEN BY THE SUSPECT ◄──► **WRITTEN BY INTERVIEWER**

WRITTEN BY THE SUSPECT	WRITTEN BY INTERVIEWER
When a person wishes to write it himself he will be asked to write out and sign the following before starting to write what he wants to say:	If the person asks the interviewer to write it for him, the officer must write out the following and ask him to sign or make his mark to it:
'I make this statement of my own free will. I understand that I do not have to say anything but that it may harm my defence if I do not mention when questioned something which I later rely on in court. This statement may be give in evidence.'	*'I......... wish to make a statement. I want someone to write down what I say. I understand that I do not have to say anything but that it may harm my defence if I do not mention when questioned something I later rely on in court. This statement may be given in evidence.'*
The exact words must be written down. Any questions - to make it more intelligible - and the answers, must be written contemporaneously. After being allowed to read the statement and asked to make any corrections. alteration or additions he wishes, he must be asked to write and sign the following:	A person who writes his own statement shall be allowed to do so in his own words except: 1. the officer may indicate to him which matters are material; or 2. the officer may question any ambiguity in the statement.
'I have read the above statement and I have been able to correct, alter or add anything I wish. This statement is true. I have made it of my own free will.'	

What is a significant statement?

CODES OF PRACTICE - CODE C 11

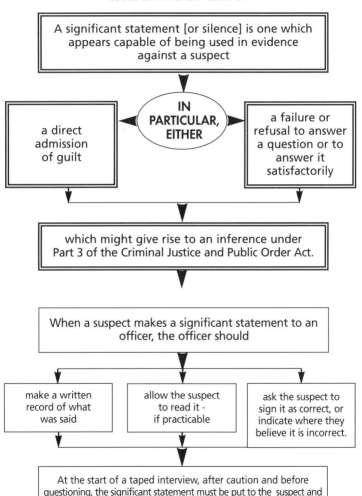

A significant statement [or silence] is one which appears capable of being used in evidence against a suspect

IN PARTICULAR, EITHER

a direct admission of guilt

a failure or refusal to answer a question or to answer it satisfactorily

which might give rise to an inference under Part 3 of the Criminal Justice and Public Order Act.

When a suspect makes a significant statement to an officer, the officer should

make a written record of what was said

allow the suspect to read it - if practicable

ask the suspect to sign it as correct, or indicate where they believe it is incorrect.

At the start of a taped interview, after caution and before questioning, the significant statement must be put to the suspect and they must be asked if they wish to confirm, deny or add anything.

NB: A written record shall also be made of any comments made by an arrested person, including unsolicited comments which are outside the context of an interview but might be relevant to the offence, and these should be dealt with in the same way as a significant statement.

When can a court draw adverse inference from an accused's failure to account for his presence at a particular place

CRIMINAL JUSTICE AND PUBLIC ORDER ACT 1994 - SECTION 37

A court or jury may draw such inferences as appear proper

▼

when a PERSON ARRESTED BY A CONSTABLE FAILS OR REFUSES to account for his presence at a particular place when requested to do so

▼

IN THE FOLLOWING CIRCUMSTANCES

▼

A person arrested by a constable was FOUND BY HIM AT A PLACE at or about the time the offence is alleged to have been committed;

▼

the arresting constable, or any other constable investigating the offence, believes that the person's presence may be attributable to his involvement in the offence;

▼

the constable informs the person that he believes his presence may be attributable to his involvement in the offence.

When can a court draw adverse inference from an accused's failure to account for incriminating evidence in his possession?

CRIMINAL JUSTICE AND PUBLIC ORDER ACT 1994 - SECTION 36

A court or jury may draw such inferences as appear proper

▼

when a SUSPECT ARRESTED BY A CONSTABLE FAILS OR REFUSES to account for possession of objects, substances or marks, when requested to do so

▼

IN THE FOLLOWING CIRCUMSTANCES

▼

The person is arrested by a constable AND there is found in his possession any object, substance or mark; OR any mark *on* any object;

▼

the arresting constable, or any other officer investigating the offence, believes that its presence may be attributable to his involvement in any offence specified by the officer;

▼

the constable informs the person arrested that he believes that the presence of the object, substance or mark may be attributable to his involvement in the offence.

NB: The object etc must be on his person; in or on his clothing or footwear; otherwise in his possession, or at any place where he is at the time of his arrest.

What police action is necessary if a suspect fails or refuses to answer questions after arrest?

CRIMINAL JUSTICE AND PUBLIC ORDER ACT 1994 - SECTIONS 36 & 37

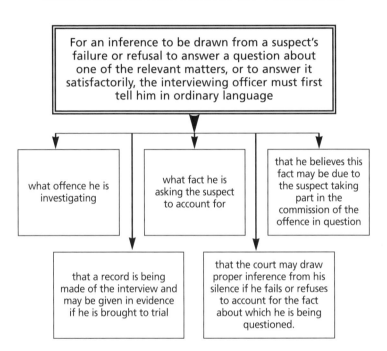

For an inference to be drawn from a suspect's failure or refusal to answer a question about one of the relevant matters, or to answer it satisfactorily, the interviewing officer must first tell him in ordinary language

what offence he is investigating

what fact he is asking the suspect to account for

that he believes this fact may be due to the suspect taking part in the commission of the offence in question

that a record is being made of the interview and may be given in evidence if he is brought to trial

that the court may draw proper inference from his silence if he fails or refuses to account for the fact about which he is being questioned.

When do you require an appropriate adult for an interview?

CODES OF PRACTICE - CODE C 11

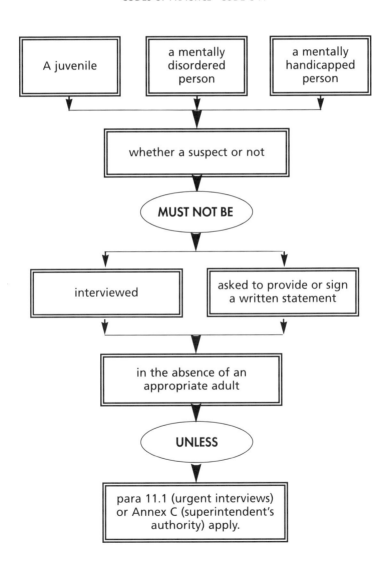

What is an appropriate adult?

CODES OF PRACTICE - CODE C 1

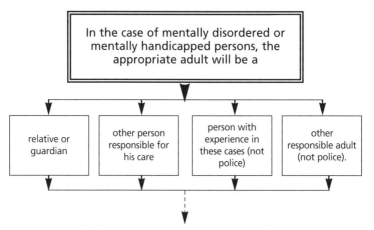

NB: It may sometimes be better have someone trained
or experienced - unless the interviewee prefers a relative.

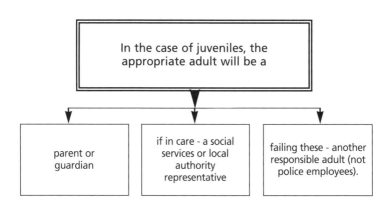

What advice can an appropriate adult be given?

CODES OF PRACTICE - CODE C 11

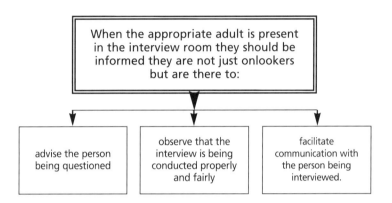

When the appropriate adult is present in the interview room they should be informed they are not just onlookers but are there to:

| advise the person being questioned | observe that the interview is being conducted properly and fairly | facilitate communication with the person being interviewed. |

Who cannot be an appropriate adult?

CODES OF PRACTICE - CODE C 1

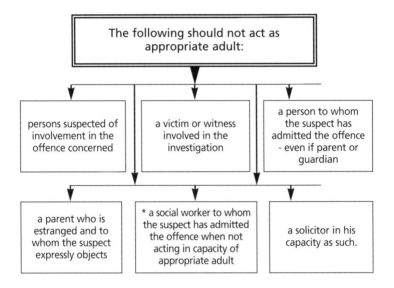

* NB: If the admission is made to the social worker *while in the capacity of an appropriate adult* they may continue as appropriate adult.

What safeguards should be taken with persons who appear to be deaf or have a speech handicap?

CODES OF PRACTICE - CODE C 13

In the event of doubt as to a person's ability to hear or speak he should be treated as having such a handicap.

The person must not be interviewed in the absence of an interpreter unless he agrees in writing.

An interpreter shall also be called if a juvenile is interviewed and the person present as appropriate adult appears to be deaf or there is doubt about his hearing or speaking ability.

The interpreter should be allowed to read any record of the interview and certify its accuracy.

What action should be taken if a person seems to have difficulty understanding English?

CODES OF PRACTICE - CODE C 13

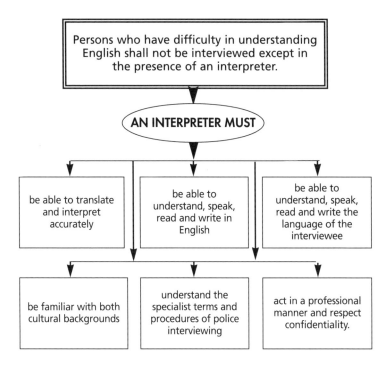

Persons who have difficulty in understanding English shall not be interviewed except in the presence of an interpreter.

AN INTERPRETER MUST

| be able to translate and interpret accurately | be able to understand, speak, read and write in English | be able to understand, speak, read and write the language of the interviewee |

| be familiar with both cultural backgrounds | understand the specialist terms and procedures of police interviewing | act in a professional manner and respect confidentiality. |

Progress of the interview with an interpreter

The interpreter shall
1. note what is said in the language of the interviewee
2. certify the record of the interview
3. allow the interviewee to read the record of interview, or read it to him
4. ask the interviewee to sign it as accurate, or indicate inaccuracies
5. after the interview, translate the record into English and certify it accordingly.

If a suspect fails or refuses to answer questions during interview, can inference be drawn from this in court?

CRIMINAL JUSTICE AND PUBLIC ORDER ACT 1994 - SECTION 34

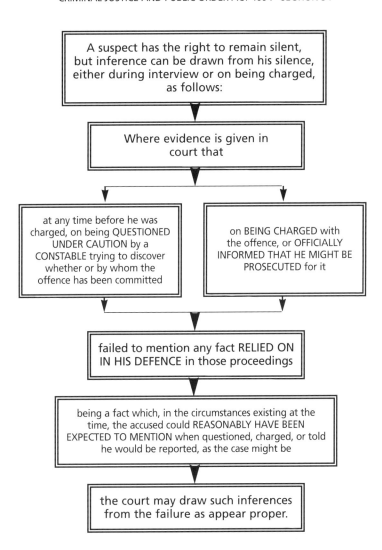

A suspect has the right to remain silent, but inference can be drawn from his silence, either during interview or on being charged, as follows:

Where evidence is given in court that

at any time before he was charged, on being QUESTIONED UNDER CAUTION by a CONSTABLE trying to discover whether or by whom the offence has been committed

on BEING CHARGED with the offence, or OFFICIALLY INFORMED THAT HE MIGHT BE PROSECUTED for it

failed to mention any fact RELIED ON IN HIS DEFENCE in those proceedings

being a fact which, in the circumstances existing at the time, the accused could REASONABLY HAVE BEEN EXPECTED TO MENTION when questioned, charged, or told he would be reported, as the case might be

the court may draw such inferences from the failure as appear proper.

A defendant need not give evidence in court, but can inference be drawn from this?

CRIMINAL JUSTICE AND PUBLIC ORDER ACT 1994 - SECTION 35

An accused person at trial has the right not to give evidence, but inference can be drawn from his silence, either during interview or on being charged, as follows:

At the close of the prosecution evidence, at the trial of any person aged 14 years or over for an offence

the court shall satisfy itself that the accused is aware that the stage has been reached at which evidence can be given for the defence and that he can, if he wishes, give evidence

AND THAT IF HE CHOOSES

not to give evidence

having been sworn, refuses, without good cause, to answer any questions

it will be permissible for the court or jury to draw such inferences as appear proper from his failure to give evidence or his refusal, without good cause, to answer any question.

Are confessions always admissible in evidence?

POLICE AND CRIMINAL EVIDENCE ACT 1984 - SECTION 76

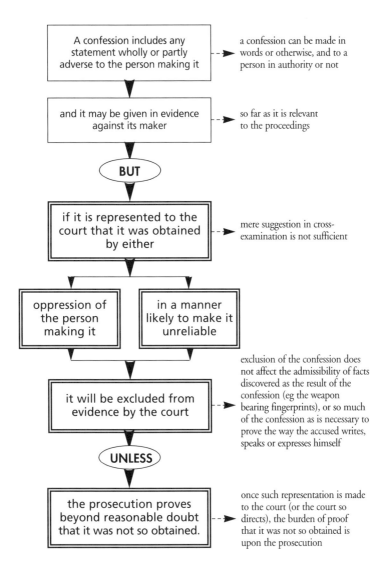

A confession includes any statement wholly or partly adverse to the person making it

→ a confession can be made in words or otherwise, and to a person in authority or not

and it may be given in evidence against its maker

→ so far as it is relevant to the proceedings

BUT

if it is represented to the court that it was obtained by either

→ mere suggestion in cross-examination is not sufficient

oppression of the person making it

in a manner likely to make it unreliable

it will be excluded from evidence by the court

→ exclusion of the confession does not affect the admissibility of facts discovered as the result of the confession (eg the weapon bearing fingerprints), or so much of the confession as is necessary to prove the way the accused writes, speaks or expresses himself

UNLESS

the prosecution proves beyond reasonable doubt that it was not so obtained.

→ once such representation is made to the court (or the court so directs), the burden of proof that it was not so obtained is upon the prosecution

Index

Directory to Part III

the New Police Bookshop

Investigative Interviewing Explained

first ed 1999, by Brian Ord and Gary Shaw
is published by the New Police Bookshop (Surrey)

To contact the publisher regarding *Investigative Interviewing Explained*
or any other NPB title, please write to:
The New Police Bookshop (Surrey), Benson Publications,
PO Box 124, Woking, Surrey GU22 9XT

Other titles from the same publisher...

Crime Patrol: to recognise and arrest criminals
first ed 1998, by Mike McBride

The Child Protection Investigators' Companion
second ed 1999, by Kevin Smith

The Human Factor: a guide to handling police informants
first ed 1999, by Tim Roberts

Police Powers: an operational guide
first ed 1999, by Alan Greaves and David Pickover

To order any of the above, write fax phone or e-mail

Brookland Mailing Services, Unit 5, Parkway Trading Estate,
St Werburghs Road, Bristol BS2 9PG.
Tel 0117 9555 215 Fax 0117 9541 485
Email npb@brookservices.demon.co.uk

Please make cheques payable to the New Police Bookshop

Available from the New Police Bookshop (East Yorkshire)...

The Custody Officer's Companion
second ed 1998, by Stewart Calligan and Paul Harper

To order *The Custody Officer's Companion* (price £16.50 inc p&p)
please write with cheques payable to
The New Police Bookshop (East Yorkshire)
PO Box 124, Goole DN14 7FH

Ann Ruffell
Leaving Home

A Pan Original

First published 1987 by Pan Books Ltd,
Cavaye Place, London SW10 9PG

9 8 7 6 5 4 3 2 1

© Ann Ruffell 1987

ISBN 0 330 29837 2

Printed and bound in Great Britain by
Richard Clay Ltd,

Chapter 1

Perhaps it was because it was a grey day that I took it so badly. It was one of those summers – you know the sort – where winter limps late into spring, which creaks on towards the end of June. Suddenly flowers bloom and fade in a day as if to make up for lost time, and, just as at the end of a fortnight you begin to think there might be a summer after all, the rain sets in and you know you're in for another long, tedious, ten-month winter.

My parents had suddenly told me that they thought it was time I left home.

'You'll be eighteen in a couple of months, Sue,' my mother said, 'and although we love having you at home we do feel it's time you learned to live on your own.'

My head was buzzing. I hadn't done anything *wrong*, or made life hell for them, or anything like that. Why, then . . .

'That's just it,' said Dad. 'You are a responsible, nice girl. Just the sort of person who would be good at coping for herself.'

But none of my friends do,' I argued in a panic. 'I just know they don't want to move out. I mean, they're too comfortable!'

'Exactly,' said Dad. 'Supposing something happened to us – no, don't say anything, I know we're not on our deathbeds yet, but accidents do happen . . . '

'Oh, come on!'

'All right, it's not very likely. At least, I hope so, anyway,' he said, twisting his mouth. 'But anyway, that's not the point. We think you ought to learn to manage for yourself. But don't worry, we'll be close at hand so that if you need help we're always here.'

'Seems a bit daft to go, then,' I muttered.

I knew I was making it difficult for them, and I heard Mum suppress a sigh.

'Try and look at it from your own point of view, love,' she said. 'Wouldn't you like to have your own place and lead your own life? Wouldn't you feel a sense of achievement looking after yourself?'

This was a bit of a dig at me, because I knew, and they knew, that I'd wasted my time at school. I'd hated it, and I'd played around – not that I was the only one – and only got one O level. They'd been disappointed at the time, I knew, because they'd expected more of me; but they'd been really good about it and said it was my own life and if I wanted to leave and find a job that was okay by them. The only thing I would never admit to them was that I found my job – working in our local paper shop – excruciatingly boring and it was only the thought of the money at the end of the week that kept me there. No, not really just the money. I really was glad I didn't have to do homework or learn stupid things about Geography or analyse books in English which I always reckoned spoiled reading them.

'I know I could look after myself,' I sulked.

'Then if you know you can, there's no problem,' said Dad in an artificially jolly but determined voice, and I knew that there wasn't much point in trying to argue any more.

I had one last try. 'I suppose they want a room each?' I said, referring to my two younger sisters Chris and Jenny.

'I've no doubt they'll be glad of some space,' Mum said tightly and instead of feeling triumphant I just felt mean.

I was still feeling ashamed of my last comment when I went up to my room a bit later on. But mostly I felt angry and upset, and shocked that they had had to ask me to leave, instead of me deciding to go myself. *None* of my friends, I muttered furiously, putting on a record at full volume, none of them have such unfeeling parents. Even if they do want to get rid of their offspring, I didn't think they'd actually get round to telling them to push off.

I couldn't concentrate on anything. I'd been knitting myself a jumper, and that evening I got into such a muddle with the pattern that I had to undo yards of it because it was complicated and I couldn't work out where I'd got up to. It wasn't *fair*.

So here I was, on a Saturday which I'd got off for once, with nothing to do but sit in my room with my knitting and watch the rain drizzling down outside my window.

Someone scratched at the door.

'What?' I growled.

''S me.'

'Which me?' though I knew perfectly well it was Jenny, ten, the youngest of us three sisters.

'This me,' she said, coming in.

'I didn't say come in,' I said, determined to be awkward, but she began talking before I'd finished.

7

'When you go,' she said rapidly, 'can I have first choice of your room?'

'For God's *sake*!' I yelled. 'Can't you wait till I've gone before you chuck me out of the house?'

'I was only asking,' she said in that injured voice which I knew so well, and she turned and went out with that all too familiar droop in her shoulders. If she thought *that* would move me, she had another think coming. She had almost closed the door when it opened again. Her head popped round, and she added, 'So long as you remember I asked first, and not Chris.'

'Get out!' I snarled.

I waited for Chris to come in, and made another mistake in my knitting pattern. Furious, I rolled it up and chucked it back into the bag before staring gloomily out of the window at the rain.

I didn't know why they were so eager to get first go at my room. Their own was much bigger, and I'd have thought they'd be arguing about which one was going to get that to herself. In fact the only advantage I could see was that my little room was at the back of the house, so you didn't get any noise from the road.

On the other hand, if it wasn't Chris at all but just Jenny, then it made more sense. I knew my little sister very well. It probably hadn't occurred to her that Chris would get the larger room if she moved out. It would be just like her to try and get in on something she thought Chris would be missing!

The thought made me giggle, and I wondered how soon Jenny would realize and start scheming to get the other room.

But I soon slumped back into feeling miserable. If

only Mike was here, I thought. Mike was my boy-friend. But he was away on a course for the weekend. 'The weekend!' I'd shrieked when he told me. 'Why the weekend, and this weekend of all weekends when I've got a Saturday off?'

'Can't do anything about it,' he'd said. 'That's when it is, and that's when I've got to go.'

Mike's been working at our local Lucas factory, in electronics, going on day-release from time to time. Then he decided he'd really rather be an engineer, so he got himself a place at college. This weekend he was on a sort of pre-course, just so that he could find out what it was all about, I think, or something like that. I wasn't looking forward to the time, which was only too soon, when he would be off to Manchester, which might as well be on another planet as far as I was concerned, because I wouldn't be able to go and see him nearly as often as I'd like.

After Jenny had gone to bed and *Dallas* was over I broached the subject again. 'I'll need things for a flat.'

I'd obviously controlled my feelings very well, because Mum looked up from her newspaper and smiled.

'I've thought of that,' she said. 'We thought you'd be more sensible to get a bed-sitter at first, so there won't be much, if anything, to buy in the way of furniture. You'll only need bed-linen, and you can take your own of course. They're usually pretty well supplied, these places. Then you can start buying the things you want for when you moved into somewhere that's unfurnished.'

'You mean I've got to go into a grotty bed-sit?' I

squeaked.

'You haven't *got* to do anything,' said my father evenly. 'We've simply suggested that it would be a good idea. If you've got savings, then by all means try and find somewhere a bit more upmarket and get your own furniture.'

He knew very well I hadn't got any savings at all – I spent all my money on clothes, records and going out with my friends.

'You're chucking me out without anything in the world, then?' I said, all my bottled-up anger bursting out.

'We're not going to throw you out onto the door-step, if that's what you mean, Sue,' said my father coldly. 'Stop being childish.'

'If I'm being childish, I'm obviously not suited to living on my own,' I muttered, just loud enough for him to hear but not as though he was supposed to.

My bad mood lasted all through the weekend, not least because I'd suddenly remembered about my birthday. Mum and Dad were throwing a party for my coming of age. A disco at our local pub.

But the whole thing was spoiled now. Instead of looking forward to my birthday party I began to dread it, seeing it as the day on which I would be old enough to go away and live on my own.

I was still feeling depressed at work on Monday.

They've got a point, my parents, about my messing around at school. If only I'd got a few O levels I might have been able to get some training instead of working in this boring shop.

I'd been there for two years. No wonder I was bored.

I suppose I was lucky to have got somewhere so near home. At least I didn't have to pay bus fares. But newsagents being newsagents you're there all day and every day, including Sundays, because we sold all kinds of groceries and sweets and cigs and things as well as papers. Mind you, I didn't work Sundays most of the time: only once a month, but I nearly always worked on Saturdays and only occasionally had that off. Like this last weekend, when Mike wasn't around to share a whole two days with me, which might have cushioned the shock.

So the customer who started moaning on Monday morning didn't exactly get my sympathy.

Why do you get the most difficult customers when you're in a bad mood yourself? If I'd been my normal cheery self I wouldn't have found them a problem at all. But today I nearly blew my top when another customer mumbled something about 'iniqueue baking' and I couldn't understand what he meant. I asked him to repeat it, and it came out just the same. Finally, in desperation, because I was on my own in the shop and there was a queue piling up, I said, 'Could you point it out, please?'

Well, I know I can be a bit stupid at times, but that look of pure dislike, plus the eyes-raised-to-heaven bit, had to be seen to be believed.

'I wouldn't have thought it was difficult to recognize *bacon*,' he said witheringly, making a great show of walking to the fridge and pointing out the packet of 'Honey Cure Bacon'.

Was my face red! Some of the waiting customers sniggered, but when he'd gone out some of them were

11

quite nice about it.

However I became more and more bad tempered as the day wore on. Sadie, the owner's wife, had asked me to sort out some packets of biscuits – or maybe it was toilet rolls – anyway, I started undoing the boxes upstairs but got side tracked, wondering what living in a place of my own would be like. I think by then I'd actually begun to think it might be nice: no little sisters to quarrel with, nobody to tell me to clean up after myself, nobody to tell me I *had* to do my ironing today because it was getting in Mum's way. Then Sadie came upstairs for something and found me doing what she thought was nothing and really told me off.

Perhaps she was at the wrong time of the month, though she's pretty old and I'd have thought she was past all that by now. Or maybe it was the menopause. Or it could have been she'd had a row with her husband that morning. Harry owns the shop, but goes around doing other, probably more interesting, things and leaves Sadie to manage the place for him. Not to mention managing me and the paper boys as well.

She grumbled on for the rest of the day.

'Sue, there are people waiting in the shop,' when I was lounging about in the last, legitimate, five minutes of my lunch hour. 'You girls these days – always have to be nagged into doing a little bit of work.'

I slumped downstairs and dealt with the two customers who had only just come in and who looked perfectly contented looking around vaguely for what they wanted, certainly not in a hurry. In fact I had to wait about ten minutes with a silly smile on my face while they poked around at the tins and crisps and biscuits.

She came down before they'd gone and gave me a sour look. Then, as they went out of the door she started up again.

'Do remember that we're here for the customers, not the other way round.' And her nagging voice went on, ' . . . service . . . always a polite smile and a cheery face . . . '

What the hell did she think I'd been doing? My face was aching from trying to smile so much.

By the end of the day I was spoiling for a fight with somebody.

As luck would have it, my sister Chris had borrowed my favourite skirt to go out in. Without asking me, and she'd already gone so I couldn't even rip it off her.

Jenny was the one who told me. Of course. Normally I'd have told her to go stick her head in a basin of water or something loving and sisterly like that, indicating I wasn't going to listen to tales, and deal with Chris myself when she got back. But I was in such a state that I raved about the house, stamping and slamming doors and having the sort of tantrum I haven't had since I was very small.

Until Mum grabbed me by the arm and told me to sit down.

'I don't want to sit down!' I yelled. 'I want my skirt!'

'Sit *down*!' bawled my mother in an even louder voice, and, because I was so surprised since she hardly ever shouted, I did just that. 'Look,' she said quietly. 'I know you're upset at what we've said, but there's no need to take it out on your sisters. Scream at us, if you like, and then we'll try and talk things over a little more calmly.'

'It's *not that*!' I shouted, knowing it was precisely that. 'It's just that I've had a rotten day at work and I – don't – like – people – borrowing – my – clothes.'

'She's a naughty girl,' agreed Mum, 'she should have asked. Now have a cup of tea and let's talk.'

'I don't want to talk,' I sulked. 'You don't want me, and that's all there is to it.'

Mum sighed as she went through to the scullery to put the kettle on. 'I thought we'd made it quite clear it's not that at all,' she said, coming back and sitting with her elbows on the half-set dining room table. 'If you'd gone away to college this would be the time you'd leave, after all.'

'I haven't gone to college,' I interrupted rudely, 'I'm at home. I don't earn much money . . . '

'You wouldn't have much money on a grant,' said Mum.

'Yes, but nobody else would either,' I argued. 'Look, can't you see it's different? All my friends still live at home. They're going to stay at home till they get married. I'll be the only one. I'll be a freak!'

'On the contrary,' said Mum, 'you'll be the only sensible, well-adjusted one. For heaven's sake, Sue, we're not sending you to Siberia! Simply suggesting you might find a bed-sitter close at hand.'

'That would be even sillier,' I retorted. 'They'll think we've fallen out or something. They'll feel *sorry* for me!'

'I'm sure they won't,' said my mother robustly. 'And

frankly I feel sorry for them if they think that. You may find they'll admire you, for having the guts to try it out on your own.'

'I'm not being given a lot of choice, am I?'

'And,' she went on as if she hadn't heard, 'as for staying until you get married – apart from the fact that you'll make a far better wife having learned how to cope, supposing you don't get married? Or not for several years? I don't want a geriatric daughter of thirty hanging about here!'

I had to laugh.

'Not even to look after you in your old age?'

'I can look after myself for a good many years yet, you cheeky thing,' she said. 'Now come and practise some living-on-your-own skills by making dinner for us while I sit down.'

'I've had a long day at work too,' I reminded her, but not nastily this time. And I went into the kitchen to poke about in the fridge and see what there was to cook. Anyway, I'd got a bit of time to kill before meeting Mike at eight.

Which reminded me – what was I going to wear since my dear sister had walked off in my favourite skirt?

Chapter 2

I was so looking forward to seeing Mike that evening that I burnt the chops and the potatoes were like rocks in the centre. That, of course, made me feel bad again because, I thought miserably as Mum and Dad cheerfully ate my disgusting meal, I really wasn't at all competent to do things by myself. And from what I'd heard of bed-sits there'd only be a gas ring, quite a different matter from the modern electric stove with temperature controls and timing pinger and fan oven that we have at home.

'The beans are nice,' said Dad pleasantly when Jenny started kicking up a fuss.

'Oh, yeah? Even I can heat up a tin!' she said scornfully.

Which didn't improve things one bit. Then when Jenny was clearing the things to wash them up I remembered: 'I suppose it hasn't occurred to my lovely sister that I might have wanted to wear my own skirt tonight.'

I began to think there might be quite a few compensations for leaving home. There wouldn't be anyone but me to complain if chops were burned or potatoes were hard. There would be no squabbling sisters. My clothes would be sacrosanct.

And now I had to decide what to wear, because I had genuinely meant to put on the skirt that Chris had made off with. I hurled things out of my drawers and wardrobe, rejecting the red dress because it needed ironing and I hadn't time, throwing aside my jeans because they were filthy, and finally, grumpily, settling for a way-out black thing which Mike didn't really like because he thought I looked too punky in it and he preferred me looking conventional. Tough, I thought, he'll just have to put up with it for once. After all, I don't dictate to him what he ought to wear.

I could see the mild disapproval in his eyes when he called round at ten to eight, but I was not in a mood for criticism and said right out, 'Can you believe it? Chris has gone off in my favourite skirt!'

'Is that why . . . ' he began, but I pushed him unceremoniously out of the door and said, 'I've got something to tell you. But first, how did your weekend go?'

He brightened up at that. 'Fantastic,' he said. 'Hard work, but fantastic. I got there on Friday night and we had a lecture straight away. I didn't understand a word. Same on Saturday. The food was good, though – better than my mother's anyway. And the first thing we did was find the bar . . . '

'You didn't understand a word? Honest?'

'Well – you know what I mean. It's all electronics, isn't it? I doubt whether the blokes telling us about it knew what they were on about most of the time. Anyway, there was this disco on Saturday night. Really good. And the bar didn't close till midnight.'

Great, I thought. Here I'd been sitting miserably at home on my first whole weekend for ages and he'd been enjoying himself.

'And I suppose you danced with a million beautiful girls,' I said sarcastically, 'or don't beautiful girls do engineering?'

'Some,' he grinned. 'But none of them were as nice as you.'

He hugged me close to him, then bent his head to give me a kiss, the first that evening.

I don't think I've described him very well. Probably because I had a sneaking jealousy of all those machine-minded girls at the disco! He's not really all that old-fashioned, or bloody-minded. And I suppose even if I dyed my hair purple or wore safety pins in my nose he'd still like me. Though I suppose he wouldn't have asked me out in the first place if I'd done that when he met me. I'm a bit conventional myself, I suppose, and the black dress I was wearing now was a bit of an accident.

He's tallish, and stocky – not fat, but sort of broad. His hair is a nice brown, and never does what he wants it to do, so he has a permanently wind-blown look that isn't at all designer-controlled, but rather scruffy! (He'd kill me for saying so – poor Mike: he always thinks he's so well turned-out and it never quite works. Not that I'd ever tell him so.)

'Where shall we go?' he said, clutching my arm tighter in his and stepping out briskly in the cold – cold! – August evening.

'Do you know what I really want?'

'What?' You could see his grey-blue eyes going all hopeful, waiting for me to suggest a cuddle in the haystacks – if there had happened to be any within forty miles of here.

'To hop on a plane and go somewhere really hot. I'm fed up with this cold and drizzle.'

'What's wrong with you?' he said. 'You're not usually like this. Something the matter?'

'Yes. But let's go somewhere warm to talk. What about the back room of the Mitre?'

'If it's not already packed,' said Mike. 'If it is, we'll probably be more private in the bar. Nothing awful, I hope? Your family all right?'

'Oh, it's nothing like that — not really,' I said. 'I mean, the family's all right, or as right as it always is. I'll tell you when we get there.'

It wasn't far to the pub, and the back room was nearly empty. Just another couple snuggling over in the far corner, so they wouldn't be interested in listening to me. Mike went to get drinks while I settled myself behind a table, itching for him to get back so that I could blurt out what my parents had said on Saturday.

'What is it, then?' he said, putting down the two glasses carefully on the table.

'I've been told to leave,' I said perkily. It was better than showing the pain.

'Leave? What? Your job?'

'No, not that, though I must say after Sadie's mood today I wouldn't have put it past her. And to be frank I wouldn't have cared. No. It's my parents. They've told me I ought to go and get a flat.'

'They *what*?'

After I'd explained it all again, and then again, he sat back with a stupefied expression on his face. 'I can't understand it,' he said finally. 'I thought your parents were . . . well, I wouldn't have thought they'd do *that* to you. I can't understand how they can be so unfeeling!'

'I suppose it's not really unfeeling. After all, they've been saying they don't want us under their feet after we're eighteen. They'll probably do exactly the same to Chris and Jenny.'

'But it all seems so bloody selfish to me,' said Mike, flexing his muscles as if he were ready to go and attack them forthwith. 'To wait till you're eighteen, and officially of age, and then say, "Right, daughter, time to go." It's like – like – ' he stuttered helplessly, 'like *animals*!'

'Oh, Mike!' I protested, laughing.

'Well, really, it is, isn't it? Mummy bird sits on the eggs for weeks, hatches out the little chicks, feeds them with worms until they're fledged, then tips them out of the nest and says, "Right, chaps, you're on your own." '

'It's not really the same,' I said. 'I haven't got to skip off the moment midnight strikes or anything like that.'

'Even so,' pursued Mike, 'they seem to be wanting to push you out as soon as possible after that. I honestly can't understand it, Sue. I thought your parents were so understanding.'

'They are,' I said fairly.

'It doesn't sound very understanding to me, to tell your eldest daughter that they don't want her any more.'

'It's not that they don't want me,' I started to argue. 'They think I ought to learn to cope for myself.'

'But you don't need to,' said Mike. 'All the other girls I know . . . '

'All the thousands!' I interjected, teasing him.

'You know what I mean — your friends, and my friends' girl-friends — they're all still at home. I'm still at home. I'd like to see my parents trying to chuck me out.'

Contrarily, I suddenly found myself sticking up for my parents. 'But you are going away. You're going to college. They don't have to. They might be fed up with you and just waiting for the excuse for all you know.'

'Men have to go away, to find jobs and that,' he countered stuffily.

'So do girls,' I said.

'Not really,' he said. 'I mean, you could stay at home, doing your little job, until you got married.'

I would have got extrememely annoyed at that patronizing 'little job' if I hadn't got scared at his mention of getting married. 'If anyone will have me,' I said jokily. Half of me wanted Mike to say, 'Will you marry me?' or something like, 'I thought, perhaps, when I've finished college . . . ' or whatever men do say when they announce their intentions. I knew I couldn't expect the kneeling-on-the-floor, flowers and fancy words type of approach. Not from Mike.

But the other half of me didn't really want to have to make a decision like that at this moment in time. I knew I wasn't going to stay in that boring shop for ever, that when I got round to it I'd go to college myself or run away to the vineyards of France for the summer, or do voluntary work in Africa, while I was still free to do so.

'You don't want to do anything else, do you?' he said, with a sort of intense look in his eyes.

'I might do,' I said, still nervous of him saying anything I might have to make decisions about.

'What could you do?' he said, rather rudely, I thought.

'Oh, I don't know,' I hedged. 'I hadn't really thought about it. But I might, that's all.'

'You'll change your mind,' he said with certainty.

'What a cheek,' I said, and drained my glass. 'What do you want? Another pint?'

'I'll get it,' he said, half standing up, but I suddenly felt that if my parents really wanted me to be independent I might as well start now.

'No. I will. I'm still at home, remember, and I do earn some money, even if it isn't a fortune. Not a lot less than you, in fact.'

'I don't really approve,' he began, but I snatched the glass from him.

'Don't be such a male chauvinist pig,' I said. 'If I want to buy you a drink, say thank you nicely, or you may never get another one.'

'Thank you nicely,' he said, and grinned from under the lock of brown hair which always insisted on falling into his eyes.

'And when I'm skint,' I said, draining my own glass of orange, 'you can come and take me out to dinner. Or buy fish and chips or something. Depending on your state of finance at the time.'

'If I'm here,' he said.

That was a point, I thought, as I went through to the bar from the snug. He was going away. I was really going to miss him, because even though he is a bit of an old stick-in-the-mud at times, we'd been going out together for the past year, and we got on well. We had the same friends, we liked the same sort of things – like disco-dancing, collecting records, and swimming.

When I got back with the drinks he started moaning on again about how unreasonable my parents were being, but I snapped, 'Oh, shut up, Mike, I'm sick of the whole subject. Let's talk about something a bit more interesting.'

He looked faintly hurt, but twirled his glass round in his hand and said, 'Well, that's what I think anyway. Listen, there's that film you wanted to see at the cinema this week. Want to go?'

I was grateful for the change of subject, and we started talking about the terrible reviews it had got in the posh papers which his parents read and the really good ones in the rubbish papers that my parents read, and the subject of moving out didn't come up again that evening.

He had to go to a class again the next day, which was Tuesday, so after dinner I went round to Judy's. Partly just for a gossip and partly to have another moan because it had been yet another difficult day at work.

'I really don't know how long I'm going to get on with that woman!' I said. 'Do you know what she said to me today?'

And so we sipped coffee in Judy's tidy (mother-tidied, I hasten to add) bedroom I told her all about Sadie's latest unreasonableness and then told her, as if by the way, about what my parents had said.

'You lucky thing!' was her first reaction.

I'd only sort of mentioned it in passing because if she'd gone on about how awful my parents were, like

Mike had, I'd probably have had a blue fit and rushed out. So what she said took me completely by surprise.

'What do you mean?'

'I've been nagging and nagging at my mother to let me go and find a flat for ages,' declared Judy. 'She just won't hear of it. She says I'm too young – she doesn't trust Sam.' (Sam is her boy-friend.) 'She knows, absolutely knows for certain, that I couldn't boil an egg without setting fire to the place. In fact she's so determined about it that she won't even let me help in the house now! I think she's scared that if I prove I'm competent she won't have a good excuse.'

'Perhaps we'd better swap parents, then,' I said feelingly.

'Why?'

'Because I'm very comfortable where I am, thank you,' I grinned. 'Oh, it isn't that, I suppose. I've no doubt I could manage as well as anyone, but it was the feeling that they didn't want me – you know?'

'I suppose it could have seemed like that,' said Judy. 'But knowing your parents – how long have I known them?'

We both drank our coffee and deliberated. 'Must be – when did we first meet?'

'End of Junior school,' said Judy. 'We'd moved and I was sitting crying in the cloakroom because I didn't know anybody and everyone else was laughing at me but you didn't.'

'So you clung onto me and I wished I'd laughed as well,' I joked.

'Don't be rotten,' said Judy.

'All right, I didn't. Must have been my natural tender

nature. And then you must have come round soon after that because I remember you coming to tea and we had tinned fish and you were sick . . . '

'Sue!'

'You were!'

'Not all over the floor, I bet,' protested Judy. 'I'd certainly have remembered that.'

'Might be a buried psychological trauma,' I grinned. 'But no, I don't even know whether you were actually sick, you just said you were.'

'Anyway, as I was trying to say. Knowing your parents, they're only doing what they think is right for you,' said Judy. 'Wouldn't it be fun to be independent?'

I suppose Judy was making sense, but I still felt hurt. 'You could be right,' I said feeling dejected. 'But you see, even though my sisters nag each other and me like crazy, I think I'd really miss them. After being with all those people, suddenly to be on my own . . . '

'I see what you mean!' said Judy. 'It's not as if it was *you* that said, "I want to see if I can do it alone." '

'Exactly,' I agreed. 'Now if I could share with someone, we could also share the cleaning . . . '

'Cleaning!' said Judy in horror. 'Still, sharing the cooking might be fun.'

'I burned the dinner yesterday,' I said.

'And I'm not allowed to so I don't know whether I could do it without burning it,' said Judy.

'You were always good at it when we did that terrible year of Domestic Science,' I reminded her.

'Oh, yeah, but there was somebody telling you what to do and reminding you it was in there if you'd forgotten.'

'I managed to burn mine, or undercook it, in spite of that. You see, I'm totally incompetent.'

'Perhaps that's why they think you ought to try it,' said Judy.

'Oh, thanks a lot! Everyone's on their side!' Then I remembered. 'Except Mike.'

'Really? Mike?'

'Yes,' I said, not wanting to explore the subject at this moment. But she nagged at me, so I said, 'He thinks I ought to stay at home and be mummy's girl until I get married.'

'Who to?'

'God knows,' I said.

'He didn't pop the question, then?' said Judy.

'To be honest,' I said, 'I don't know what I'd have said if he had. All right, suppose you were being proposed to by this fabulous millionaire – you know, really nice, good-looking, sexy – how's he going to do it?'

So we passed the time chatting about our dreams and desires, and I didn't have to talk about Mike and his feelings any more. Because the more I thought about it (and probably Judy's reaction had a lot to do with this) the more I thought my parents were right and that he was quite, quite wrong.

Chapter 3

And then there was no time to think because the day of my party drew nearer, and I was working all week, including Wednesday, until Saturday, so I could have a lie in on Sunday and not have to go to the shop.

'Anything I can do?' asked Judy, coming round on the Friday evening. Mike, who loathed domesticity, had gone swimming.

'Cut up this onion,' said my mother instantly, storming about with a red face because she couldn't get both turkeys into the oven at the same time.

'Any particular shape?' asked Judy.

'Make them into little men with bows round their necks,' I said sarcastically. 'Stop *fussing*, Mum, we can cook one tomorrow morning.'

'But then it won't cool in time for me to cut it,' she wailed. 'I wanted them both done this evening so that . . . '

'Let me take one home and do it in ours,' said Judy.

'There's no need . . . I'm going to put it in as soon as this one's done and I'll just put the alarm on and get up in the middle of the night . . . '

'You'll do no such thing,' said Judy, taking charge of both Mum and the turkey. 'I'll be back in half an hour. Meanwhile, I'll let Sue do the onions.'

'I really can't allow your mother to use her electricity . . . ' began my mother, but Judy stepped out of that one neatly by saying, 'It's gas,' and carried off the beast in its too-small roasting tin (another thing that was upsetting Mum).

'There you are, you see,' I said to her when Judy had gone, 'if I take after you just think what it will be like when I'm on my own. Chaos unlimited!'

'You won't be cooking for forty,' she snapped, 'not yet awhile, anyway.'

'I'd thought of a housewarming,' I said slyly.

'Then tell them to bring their own food,' she said. 'Now get out of my way while I – while I –'

'You see, you haven't got anything to do just yet,' I said. 'Come and sit down and I'll make you a coffee. Where's Chris and Jenny?'

'Gone to youth club,' said my mother. 'I just couldn't bear them hanging about my heels, stealing bits, and all three of you would row.'

'Oh, come on, Mum, we don't always. I bet they've both gone out in my clothes, too. I still haven't found out where Chris went in my skirt!'

'Oh, I can tell you that,' said Mum, allowing herself to be sat down. 'She's got a boy-friend.'

'Chris! My little sister! I don't believe you.' I filled the kettle and cleared a dozen bowls out of the way to set it down somewhere where I could plug it in.

'And don't you move anything,' she called through. 'I've got everything organized.'

'Looks pretty disorganized to me,' I said disdainfully. 'It's only bowls, and they're empty.'

'Yes, but I won't know who they belong to!' wailed my mother, and came through again to try and put them back where they were.

'*They'll* know who they belong to,' I said patiently.

'Stop fussing. When it's all done and washed up you can invite them in for a sherry and display the lot, like an auction. Then if they make off with the wrong one it's not your fault.'

'Stop being so clever,' said my mother. 'Okay, you win, I'll go back and sit down, but not for long – there's a lot to do.'

'There's a lot we can't do,' I said. 'You can't have limp lettuce hanging about all day tomorrow.'

'I'm not that stupid,' said Mum, 'but the rice salads have to be done and put in the fridge. Oh – I haven't even *cooked* the rice! It'll be too hot! I wish your father was here – he's the only one who can cook rice without it turning into porridge.'

'Come to that, where is he?' I said. 'Typical man, disappearing when there's work to be done.'

'Some meeting or other,' she said. 'Why didn't you have your birthday on a more practical day?'

'For someone who works in a maternity hospital, Mum, you don't seem very knowledgeable about the facts of life,' I teased. 'Or did you think babies came from under gooseberry bushes? And if they did, I'd have thought it was your look out if you picked me out on an inconvenient day!'

Actually, Mum doesn't do any nursing or anything like that. She doesn't really need to know any of the facts of life for her job. She's the person at the reception who sorts out all the pregnant mums. Mind you, she comes home with some funny stories sometimes. And a few sad ones. There's always some drama going on in the maternity unit. And this was why she was flapping now, because, as is the way when you've got something extra to do, she had to work tomorrow morning.

'Coffee,' I said, handing it to her. 'Now tell me about this boy-friend of Chrissie's.'

'Nothing to tell,' said Mum. 'She just came in from school, said she didn't want anything to eat because she was going to the pictures with this boy. Then she went upstairs and had hysterics because she hadn't anything to wear.'

'She never has,' I said, marvelling. 'She's not interested.'

'She is now,' said Mum. 'About time, too.'

'I keep thinking of her as a baby,' I said, 'just because she's always shared her room with Jenny, I suppose. But she's nearly sixteen, of course.'

'Another birthday!' groaned my Mum, then got up so suddenly her coffee nearly spilled. 'I'm sorry, Sue, but I really can't sit down. I'll drink it while I'm doing things. I must put on that rice. If I've got enough saucepans.'

There were enough, and between us we even managed to cook it without the whole lot boiling all over the stove, and, what's more, it came out quite by accident into the sort of fluffiness which usually only Dad can manage. Well, one saucepan-full didn't, but we were so pleased with the rest we didn't care, thinking we'd leave that lot for emergency in case there wasn't enough.

'I hope all these people you've invited turn up,' Mum said darkly, scalding herself on boiling steam and swearing, 'or we'll be eating rice salad for the next fortnight.'

'We could give it away.' I giggled, chopping onions

30

like crazy until my eyes watered. 'Where's Judy? I was saving these for her. They don't make her cry so much with her contact lenses.'

'Ugh, don't talk about eyes,' shuddered Mum, running the scalded wrist under the cold tap.

'I hope you don't screech like that every day at work!' I mocked.

'I don't see the nasty bits,' she said. 'I'm just a paper slave. Now, if you'll do those peppers – nice and small – there should be plenty of colour.'

It looked pretty good on the chopping board when I'd finished, and then Judy was back saying everything was under control her end and her Mum would store it in her fridge overnight so that we could collect it in the morning.

'I hadn't thought where I was going to put it,' said my mother, aghast.

'God! The organization in this family!' I said.

'Never again!' said Mum. 'When your sisters have their coming of age parties they can have cheese and beer, unless I've got round to working full time and can pay someone else to do it.'

'You'll have forgotten by then,' said Judy comfortably. 'Or we'll be so competent we'll take over the job.'

'You must be joking,' I said. 'Anyway, you'll still be at home and thoroughly incompetent.'

'You think you're going to be any better?' she said with a raised eyebrow and a sideways, cheeky look at my Mum. 'Anyway, I'm working on it.'

'Oh?'

'That's all,' she said. 'Just working on it. Now, what

else is there?'

By the time everyone came home we were sitting in front of the TV with our feet up, feeling exhausted. But there were a satisfying lot of things crowding the fridge, or simply sitting in cool places like my room with cling-film over them, while wafting through the house was the Christmassy smell of roasting turkey.

'Celebration?' said Dad as he came in and made straight for the sherry bottle, handing out glasses to Judy and me as well as Mum, while Chris made for the Coke.

'What could there be to celebrate?' Mum said.

'Getting rid of a daughter, perhaps?' he smiled. His eyes go all crinkly at the corners when he's making his little jokes, and I knew he didn't really mean it, not nastily at any rate. In any case I was too tired to rise to anything just now.

'Somebody's birthday, maybe?' said Mum, waiting until all the glasses were filled before raising hers. 'Happy birthday, darling!'

'Oh, crikey, so it is. I'd forgotten!' And they all yelled with laughter, as if we'd been doing all this work for some entirely different reason than my birthday party. 'Actually, it isn't, not for another two hours, but thanks, all the same.'

The food was fabulous. Just as well – the party was so slow to start, as most of my friends didn't turn up until just before the pubs closed. Well, not *my* friends exactly, but some of the others that my friends had said they wanted to bring, if you see what I mean.

Mum and Dad had asked when we wanted to have

the food, and I'd said about nine, because it seemed to me we'd have more time for dancing afterwards. But when these people didn't come and didn't come, and we'd waited for them so that they didn't miss the food, Mum finally said, 'I'm going to start serving out. Go and tell the disc-jockey, after the next record they can come through.'

When everyone had eaten enough, and most of the late-comers had arrived and rushed over for the remains of our neighbour's puddings, and the girls were beginning to sit on boys' laps, Mum and Dad thought they'd beat a tactful retreat home to the kitchen and the washing-up. Jenny, who wanted to stay, was dragged off with them.

Chris was still there, sitting next to the boy she'd gone out with *in my skirt* and whom she'd asked if she could invite. So far they hadn't done anything except sit holding hands, with soppy looks on their faces.

'Great party,' mumbled Mike, his lips nuzzling against my neck, and I stopped worrying about anyone else for a bit.

'Let's dance,' I said, because there was this fabulous record that was my favourite at the moment.

'I'm quite comfortable where I am,' mumbled Mike, hugging me closer.

'Oh, come on, it's my birthday.'

'You're of age now. You're allowed to kiss me,' he said, and I realized that he was beginning to get slightly drunk. Though I didn't think he'd had more than me. However, now I came to think of it, I'd been so busy rounding people up to get their food that I didn't remember him coming to get something to eat.

'Didn't you have any dinner?' I said.

'Don't tell me it's been and gone?' he giggled.

'Oh, Mike, honestly! Couldn't you stay sober just for me?'

'At a party? Don't be silly. Who wants to stay sober at a party?'

'Well, I want to dance. Come on. It might sober you up.'

'As your majesty pleases. After all. It is your birthday.'

'Quite,' I said coldly.

However, once on the floor he seemed to come to life, and, with his inhibitions gone, he danced around and we had a really good time for the next three or four records. Then he flopped down and pulled me down beside him.

'You know,' he said, 'I really think your parents are pigs pushing you out like that. I wouldn't let a daughter of mine go and live on her own at eighteen.'

'For heaven's sake, Mike, are you saying there's one law for men and another for women?'

'Lovely women,' he mumbled, and closed his eyes, grabbing me again with a grip that was surprisingly hard considering he was getting pretty drunk.

'Let go, you idiot, you're embarrassing me.'

'Why? Everyone else is.'

It was true. But I've never liked to cuddle in full public view. It was all right in private, like down by the canal where we walked sometimes, when Mike's kisses were sweet and lovely and sent shivers all through me. But now, even in the warm pink light, even with the

34

noise of pop groups from the disco, not with all my friends watching.

And I didn't like the smell of his breath. Probably if I'd had a drink myself I wouldn't have have noticed, but I'd only had Cokes all through the evening. I'm not trying to say I disapprove of drink. Far from it. I like to go out to the pub as much as anyone else. And if it hadn't been for the fact that I hadn't had any alcohol myself that evening it probably wouldn't have hit me that Mike really did drink a lot and I didn't like the person he turned into when he was a bit drunk.

'Don't, Mike,' I begged.

'You see,' he said thickly, 'I want my woman waiting for me. Not all independent, like you want, or your parents want. I want to know you're there waiting for me. If you go and live in a flat, you might meet someone else . . . '

'I'm just as likely to meet someone else at work or something,' I said sharply.

'No, no,' he said waving a languid arm. 'Not at home. They can keep you safe there.'

'Mike, for God's sake go and sober up,' I said. 'You're getting maudlin. Not to mention really silly.'

'Can't see why they want to get rid of you, lovely girl that you are.' And he made another lunge, which I skidded away from, along the seat.

'It's totally unreasonable,' he pleaded, 'to sling a girl out of her home, after all these years, as if you hadn't done anything for them.'

'Don't be so stupid, Mike,' I said. 'It's not like that at all.'

But Mike in this mood was not to be argued with. 'If I had any say in it, I'd go and tell them just what I think.'

'You'll do no such thing,' I said. 'Yes, they've cared for me, for all these years, and it's about time I went and cared for myself. Their duty towards me is over.' It sounded horribly pompous, even to me, but all that nonsense Mike was saying made me really stiff and prim.

'Duty!' he said. 'A parent's duty is never over. They're pigs, I tell you.'

'Don't talk about my parents like that,' I said, really upset because this was the second time he'd called them pigs. Once you can forgive, as an expression of intense emotion, but twice . . . I was full of a sudden unexpected loyalty towards them, full of a huge appreciation of their caring, and I thought I knew why they were gently persuading me it was a good thing to try it out on my own now. It wasn't because they didn't like me being around. It wasn't because they were fed up with this caring business. It was *because* they cared that they wanted me to stand on my own two feet.

I told Mike this.

'And if you go on being rude about them I don't think I really want to know you,' I said, feeling the tears build up behind my eyes in a hot, painful burst.

'All right. If that's what you think. Then you don't really want me here. I know when I am not welcome.'

'It's not that . . . ' I began. But it was useless. Mike got up, staggered a little, and with almost comic dignity walked out of the room, past the bouncer at the door, and into the night.

I made myself stand still. But as soon as he'd gone, without so much as a backward glance, I turned and looked round my party, mouth set in a smile, free, now, to go and talk to my guests. There were plenty of other boys around, after all. I'd invited them, hadn't I? Good riddance to Mike, if he wanted to behave like that.

But they were all occupied. They had all come with someone. Chris gave me a little smile and came up to me, holding hands with the boy she'd held hands with all evening.

'It's all right, we're going straight home,' she said, and her face told me how happy she was.

My little sister.

Oh, well. I felt like that once.

I looked for Judy. My best friend. She was over in the circle of light by the DJ, dancing with Sam. She had the same dreamy, happy look on her face that Chris had. But she'd been going out with Sam for years. How did she manage to *stay* looking like that?

'Great party, Sue,' said Donna. She was with some-one as well. Alec, I think. Or was it Kev? I didn't know either of them very well, and at that moment I wasn't sure which was which.

And I didn't care.

Everybody. With somebody. Except me.

I suppose I went out fairly normally. I don't remember. All I remember is the empty trestle tables, slightly stained on the tablecloths the hotel had kindly provided for us. Past those tables, towards the ladies' loo.

Where I sat and bawled my eyes out.

Here I was, the person who was having an eighteenth birthday party, a coming of age party. Me. By myself. And everyone was enjoying themselves. Fantastic. Only I wasn't, and I was the most important person, ignored by everyone.

I had a really good wallow in self-pity. It was a good job Judy came to the ladies' after the end of the next record.

'Sue? What's the matter, Sue?'

Her arms were round my shoulders, patting me, holding out tissues to mop my tears.

'Come on, it's a great party. What's up? You can't sit here bawling. Everyone wants to sing "Happy Birthday to You"!'

'Oh, God, no!' I choked, and tried to laugh. 'How corny.'

'That's better. What's wrong, anyway? Someone said something nasty?'

'Mike,' I choked.

'Oh, no. Really? I thought he looked a bit sloshed. Stupid bloke! Tell Auntie Jude all about it.'

'It wasn't,' I snuffled, 'I mean – not really – it was –'

'Go on.'

'About my parents. He was rude about them. Said horrible things.'

'Your parents?' said Judy, mystified.

'Yeah. Remember, I told you. Only I probably didn't, not much. Because they're throwing me out. Or that was what he said. He said they were pigs, uncaring – you know. I couldn't bear it, and I yelled back.'

'So he pushed off,' said Judy, understanding. 'I like Mike, Sue, as you know, but there are times when he can be a bit off. You know what I mean?'

'Oh, it was really because he's had a bit too much to drink,' I said, scrubbing my face with the shreds of tissue and ruining what was left of my make-up. 'I don't really like him much when he's like that. And he didn't really approve of what they said, about learning to cope on my own. He doesn't want me to know how to cope on my own, I gather.'

'Possessive?' said Judy.

'Not exactly *possessive*, though he is a bit, but sort of, not thinking a woman ought to be able to do anything by herself. As if – ' and I tried to work out exactly how I thought Mike thought, 'as if it would be lowering to his own esteem if I could do some things that he wanted to be the only one to do,' I finished in a bit of a muddle.

'My God, you should have done A level Psychology,' laughed Judy.

'Might have been more successful at that than O level in anything!' I said ruefully. 'You know, Jude, I think my parents are right. I do need to get out, to stop leaning on people and become a person in my own right.'

'And finish with Mike?'

I'd never thought of that as an answer. It was almost too shocking to think about. But I suppose sometimes it takes a friend to jerk you out of your complacent self and think about what you're doing with your life. Did I *really* want Mike? There were times when I liked him very much. Sometimes I even thought I loved him. I had thought that when he saw me happy in my own little flat or bed-sit he would come round to my way of thinking. But now that Judy had made me see him so clearly, I knew, sadly, that he wouldn't.

But Judy was speaking. 'So we talked and talked about it and I finally persuaded . . . '

'Will you start all that again?'

'My parents. I told them about *your* parents and how they thought, and my Mum has a great deal of respect for your Mum, and they came round. That's all.'

'About you going to live in a flat?'

'Just that,' said Judy, showing all her attractive teeth in pleasure. 'On one condition.'

'Yes?'

'That I share it with you. Sorry, but that's their final word.'

I could feel my mouth stretching in a grin to match hers. I just couldn't believe it. 'We're stuck with each other, then?'

'So long as you don't snore,' she said cautiously.

'Me?' I squeaked indignantly. 'You've always said you sleep like the dead and it would take fifty earthquakes to wake you, so I can't see it's going to matter much if I *do* snore, which I certainly do not. How about you? I tell you the faintest noise from afar will disturb my sleep, and if you snore I'd be able to hear it three streets away.'

'I can't, then, or you'd have heard already,' said my friend, who lives, in fact, three streets away from me.

'Jude, that's marvellous,' I said. 'Not you snoring, you fool, about sharing! I must admit I was feeling a bit worried about being all on my own.'

'There's another condition as well.'

'I know,' I groaned, 'no boys after seven o'clock in

40

the evening – though why parents assume you can't be immoral or whatever it is they call it in daylight, but have to wait for sinful night, I really don't know.'

'Wrong,' said Judy. 'Try again.'

'No? I bet that will come into it somewhere.'

'They just want it to be fairly near, that's all,' said Judy, and stood aside for someone else coming into the loo, which made me realize we'd been there talking for rather a long time and it was probably time we went back to the party.

'London's near compared to Siberia,' I said, 'but I suppose we know what they mean.'

'Look at it this way,' said Judy, 'if we're nearer home than the launderette . . . '

'I doubt if my parents would see it that way,' I said, 'but we might persuade your mother to take my dirty underclothes as well. Oh, Jude, I'm really, really pleased. Do you think we'll get on?'

'Don't go too wild at the idea yet,' she cautioned. 'I'm pretty sure I've persuaded them, but anything could go wrong.'

'It can't possibly,' I said firmly, and taking Judy by the arm, completely forgetting that it was *me* that was upset and needed cheering up, I steered her out into the party.

Someone must have been watching by the supper tables, because almost as soon as I got into the room the record faded out and there was this really terrible one of *Happy Birthday to You* and everyone yelled it out even louder than the speakers, if that was possible.

From then on I wasn't alone for a second. All the boys, whoever they'd come with, queued up to dance with me, some of them twice, and I can truthfully say I didn't miss Mike one bit.

I did think of him again, however, when the last record had been played and the last reluctant guest had been ushered out of the door, leaving Judy and Sam and myself to do a quick whip-round in case there were any of our plates or pieces of cutlery left hiding beneath tables or down the sides of chairs. It was worth doing, because we found two plates and a spoon belonging to our next-door neighbour.

'God, look at the time,' I said slightly muzzily to Judy. It was only tired muzz, because as I don't like the taste of alcohol very much I'd only had a small cider to go with the Cokes during the evening. That's one thing I will say for Mike: he's never tried to make me feel small or young or anything because I don't drink much. I can have a glass of sherry with the family, or of wine when it's a celebration, but otherwise I don't really like it. The only thing is, when Mike is on a binge I feel really bored, because people can be so tedious when they're drunk. Take tonight, for instance – he'd never have gone on like that if he'd been stone cold sober. I wished he didn't drink quite so much, but I don't suppose he'd listen to me if I asked him. And I wished he'd give me the same respect by not telling *me* what I ought to do.

'Time? said Judy. 'It's only one o'clock.'

'Only? I like my beauty sleep.'

'You're not one of those people . . . ' she said, mock-horrified, raising her eyebrows to her highlighted fringe.

'You can do what you like,' I said, 'have parties

round my bed, let the neighbours batter the ceiling down complaining about the decibels of Status Quo, cook chips or whatever you like, so long as you stop by half past midnight. Then you'll have to go somewhere else to do it.'

'So long as you don't tell her mother she's gone,' said Sam, and dropped the spoon into my coat pocket, handing me the two plates at the same time. 'She needs to feel secure in the knowledge that you'll rescue her from murderers and rapists.'

'No chance,' I said, 'I'd be too busy running. But I wish you hadn't said that. I probably won't be able to sleep worrying about it.'

We made sure we had everything, then walked past the yawning bouncer at the door, saying thank you to everyone, including the disc-jockey who'd finished packing up in an incredibly short space of time.

Judy and Sam left me at the door.

'Oh, Sue, I do hope they mean it! I'm so looking forward to it,' she said.

'What? Rape and murder?' joked Sam.

'For God's sake don't say that to my Mother,' she scolded him. 'Don't even joke about it. No, I'm looking forward to being me, because that's really what it's all about, isn't it?'

Chapter 4

That's what it would have been all about, if only we could have found a place to be ourselves in.

After Judy's parents had been to see *my* parents, and pursed their lips and looked doubtful and all the things they thought they ought to look, they finally made up their minds that Jude was really past cradle age and able to do her own washing up.

Their conditions made things a bit difficult, however. Though Judy herself would have lived under a railway arch or rented a park bench simply to get away from home, I was a bit more choosy, and of course, Jude's parents were *extremely* fussy.

And it didn't help working at weekends so often. If I went to an agency on my day off, Jude would still be handing out packets of money to people at the bank, and if she found the ideal place on a Saturday, I would still be handing out packets of chewing gum and cigarettes to people in the shop.

And they all cost too much anyway.

'We'll have to have one bedroom, that's all,' I said glumly. 'We can toss a coin for who's going to have a bed-sit in the living room and who's having the other room.'

'Don't suppose there's much difference,' said Judy. 'They'll all be converted from bedrooms or living rooms anyway.' We'd been out during the evening, looking at an unfurnished flat, but it was really too much for us to pay. 'Do you think we ought to look at furnished ones? They're probably cheaper.'

'They ought to be more,' I said, 'if they're throwing furniture in as well.'

'Yeah, but Sam told me it's because they can throw you out of furnished places, but not out of unfurnished.'

'Oh, great,' I said. 'How to make you feel really wanted!'

I was feeling bitter about Mike, who refused to come flat hunting with me, or even to listen when we discussed it. He didn't even approve of my going if I shared with Judy, and we'd had another row about *that*.

'If I'd gone to college or something,' I said to him, 'I'd be sharing a flat with a friend. Where's the difference?'

He mumbled something about friends' boy-friends and boy-friends' friends, which I refused to understand, and then he said, 'You haven't gone to college,' as if this clinched it. I thought he was being insulting, the way he said it, as well as showing a complete lack of understanding.

And that row was a pity, because after the party he'd been round to apologize for getting in a temper and storming off, and for days after he'd been really sweet and nice – the old Mike whom I'd fallen for in the first place.

Anyway, since Mike wouldn't come with me, Judy tactfully asked Sam to keep out of the way while we were trudging round looking at anything that sounded remotely affordable, and instead we met up at one of our houses afterwards for coffee. It wasn't very satisfactory: Mike was obviously busting to go to the pub by then, and I refused because I wanted to save up every last penny, and I was beginning to feel bored with the constant having to go to the pub, as if there wasn't anywhere else to be.

I'm not really being prudish about this, honest. Only he'd annoyed me once too often, and I said to Mum one evening that I thought it was about time I told him I didn't like him boozing so much.

'You're getting very aggressive, aren't you?' said my Mother. It was the evening after one when we'd been looking at two flats, one of which was so grotty that it would probably fall down if you breathed out, and the other which we shouldn't have bothered to go and see as we knew it was too expensive anyway. This evening there had been nothing to go and see at all, not even a cowshed.

'Am I? It just seems fair to me.'

'If anyone else goes on about being *fair* I'll suffocate them,' said Chris darkly from a corner where she was curled up with a book. 'I'll be glad when you've gone, Sue, and I can have a room to myself. With Jenny even if I split things so evenly down the middle you could measure it with a micrometer she'd still find a molecule of difference and make a scene about it.'

'She's growing up,' said my Father undulgently.

'You don't say that when I complain,' said Chris. 'If I didn't have to go to school and I had a job, for two pins I'd go and get a flat with Sue.'

'Where you'd quarrel just like you do at home,' said Mum. 'All three of you are getting far too quarrelsome. Calm down a little.'

'We're standing up for our rights,' I said. 'It's your

46

own fault, Mum. You've got us to fly the nest, you must expect us to be able to fight for ourselves.'

'Yes, but not . . .' began Mum.

'You can't have it both ways,' said Chris. She swung herself out of her chair. 'Well, since I'm supposed to be doing brainy things at school I'd better get on with the homework. At least I'll get a better job than Sue.'

'You'll be lucky,' I sneered. 'There are university graduates who can't get jobs these days.'

'I will,' said Chris with certainty.

And she would. There was the difference between my sister and me. What she wanted she got. And all that about Jenny wasn't a contradiction. She puts up with just so many of Jenny's whims and then calmly gets her own way, almost without anyone noticing.

Like pinching my skirt.

And she was dead right about getting a better job than me. Even if I had millions of O levels and she hadn't any, she'd get a better job than me. Only since it suits her to get O levels so that she can get the sort of job she wants, she'll do it.

I couldn't help wondering whether I had the wrong attitude.

Oh, well, there wasn't much I could do about it at this moment. What I was doing now was saying to Mum and Dad, 'I don't think we'll be able to get anywhere nice, not on our sort of money, not even with two of us.'

'No, I didn't think you would,' said Dad.

'Then why didn't you . . .' But of course they both had told me: Lower your sights, unless you have capital . . .

Capital? Ha ha. Twenty quid, at the last count.

'It would be easier if we could find somewhere a bit further away,' I said. 'I wish Jude's parents hadn't given us a limit of a hundred yards' distance from home. It's too expensive round here. Sorry Dad, but you're too posh for us!'

'Better move, I suppose,' he joked. 'Where would you prefer to have your slum?'

'I don't think we're even going to get a kitchen to ourselves,' I said gloomily to Judy after an exhausting evening, looking at places that were too expensive as usual. 'How do they get people to pay that much? If they've got all that income, why don't they buy a whole house?'

'Same reason as us – they haven't saved up enough,' said Judy.

'Impossible to save up any if you've got to pay that kind of rent,' I grumbled. 'Okay, what do you say we cut our losses and do the bed-sits next week?'

'If there are any,' said Judy. 'The Polytechnic starts then.'

My heart did a funny little jump. Mike started college next week too. At a different Poly, miles away from me.

'Anywhere we could afford will have been snapped up already,' Judy went on.

'Now then, think positive,' I said, willing myself to do just that and to keep my mind off Mike's imminent departure. Instead I made myself think of Chris and what she would do. 'We're going to get the best bed-sit in town, right?'

'Right,' said Judy.

*

'Perhaps there's something in this positive thinking stuff,' I said to Judy, amazed after we'd paid up our first month's rent in advance for what must have been very nearly the best bed-sit in town.

We had been lucky – or positive, Chris would have said. I had been really organized for a change and had seen an advert in the local paper just as it arrived in the shop. So Jude and I went along to the bed-sit, and the landlady told us that a prospective student hadn't got good enough A levels to go the Poly, and wasn't taking the room after all.

It really was a nice room. Probably if we hadn't seen so many revolting places during our trudges around the area we might have turned up our noses, but by contrast, it was paradise.

And we had a week to move in.

'Well, we don't *have* to move in, I suppose,' I told Mike, 'it's just that we've paid for it, so we might as well. I'd only have to pay Mum and Dad as well, and I can't afford that. I mean, I'll probably feel like eating as well.'

'But I thought we'd spend all my last week together,' said Mike like a sulky child.

'We still can,' I said. 'Why not spend it helping us move in? I'd really appreciate the help.' If this came out a bit sarcastically, I thought I had good reason.

'I don't think I really want to,' said Mike distantly, and I felt like crying. It wasn't *my* fault I was moving, and there didn't seem much point in being miserable about it if I was going to have to anyway, I reasoned. But he seemed to think the very fact that I was looking forward to it was being disloyal to him.

I think Mike was even more against our move because he couldn't see me when *he* wanted any more. He'd got used to ringing me up and saying, 'How about the cinema? Pick you up at seven', or 'Jeff's got a party on Saturday. I'll be round at eight.' This last fortnight, when he'd done that, I'd said, 'Sorry, Mike, we're flat hunting.'

'But you can't flat hunt all the time,' he'd protested to begin with.

'No. I'm at work. That's why I've got to do it in the evening,' I said, totally reasonably I thought.

'You're still determined, aren't you? Doesn't it occur to you that if you stand firm your parents would back down and let you stay?'

'Mike, hasn't it got into you thick head yet? I *want* to go and live in a flat with Judy.'

We sat stiffly over our coffee in my parents' kitchen, not talking. I didn't know why he seemed to have changed so much. I'd really loved him a lot, and it was such a silly thing to get in a huff about – especially when he wasn't going to be around for long now so we couldn't take our time about making up.

A sudden thought hit me, that Mike had been even less enthusiastic when I'd said I was going to share with Judy. My mind doesn't work this sort of way normally, but Judy and I had been talking about a friend of ours who'd got pregnant by accident, and it now occurred to me that Mike might have come round to the fact that I would be on my own, which might be an advantage if he wanted to seduce me. But if I was going to share with Judy then he was going to find the seduction thing just as difficult as if I were still at home.

My thoughts were rambling. Was it Mike who made me so confused? I really didn't know what I felt about him. Only a few months – weeks – ago, I'd have said I was totally, gloriously, in love with him, and that I'd only have to stick it out at home with Mum and Dad for the time he'd be at college, then he'd come back and sweep me off my feet and we'd get married in a shower of confetti and . . .

Perhaps it wasn't Mike who had changed, but me.

'Don't get upset,' he said, putting his arm round me. 'I don't want to help you get your stuff in, because I still don't think it's right for you and it upsets me, but I'll come round when you're settled. Okay?'

'You won't be able to,' I said, managing to keep the tears at bay. 'You'll have gone.'

'Great – then I won't have to see you there. It's only because I don't want to see you in some scruffy place. I like thinking of you here, where I'm used to seeing you. I don't want to see you – well, in a kitchen of your own, I suppose, if I'm not there to share it with you.'

'I don't know whether this is the right time to tell you,' I choked, trying to make a joke, 'but I can't cook!'

'About this cooking,' said Judy when we next met.

'There must be a book on it,' I said.

'I'm not joking,' she said. 'I'm absolutely serious.'

'I'm not joking either,' I said. 'Don't worry. We can use a tin opener, can't we?'

'Good thing my mother can't hear you saying that,'

said Judy. 'She's been threatening to haul me back home if I so much as look at the outside of a tin with lustful eyes.'

'Talking of lust,' I remarked, 'aren't we supposed to be meeting the blokes half an hour ago?'

'Let them wait,' said Judy with a lordly wave of her hand. 'I've hung about for Sam often enough. It will do him good to hang about for me for a change. They might be swapping recipes for us.'

'Ha bloody ha,' I said. 'Swapping dirty stories, more like, considering they're in the Mitre and probably have been since opening time.'

I was glad Sam and Judy were around, because I think I was afraid of it all ending if we were by ourselves. Perhaps we'd find each other again, I thought, when Mike came back from college and had got used to the fact of me being in a flat.

Or, which might be worse, I might find myself married to him without having thought about it properly first.

'I wonder if he's worried about going to college,' I remarked to Judy as we walked to the Mitre.

'Who? Mike? Could be. I would. But I bet if you asked him he'd say he wasn't.'

'The macho thing again,' I sneered. 'Why do they think they've got to be macho? I'm sure there aren't any girls who really want them to be. I'd much rather talk about interesting things than drink and throw people about.'

'He doesn't hit you, does he?' said Judy, shocked at the very idea.

'Not so far,' I said. 'He'd better not, that's all. No, I

meant all that muscle stuff – I wouldn't mind if it was useful, like helping move stuff into a new flat.'

Judy glanced at me, hearing the bitterness in my voice, but wisely said nothing else.

And Mike was in a really bloody mood when we got there.

'Guess what,' I said in a jolly, chatty way, 'we've discovered something interesting about each other. *Neither* of us can cook!'

'Then you've been pretty stupid, haven't you?' said Mike, really seriously, glaring at us.

'Oh, Mike, don't be such a wet blanket,' I said. 'What's up with you, anyway? Sorry we're late, but we were talking.'

'About your wonderful flat, no doubt,' said Mike sourly.

Judy raised her eyebrows. 'What do you want to drink, Mike? No, Sam, I'll get them. Sue?'

Sam went with her up to the bar.

'I'm sorry,' I said again, 'but it's not always possible to be on time. Anyway, it's about the first time I ever have been late.'

'Shows it is always possible, then, doesn't it?' said Mike disagreeably.

'Sam isn't complaining,' I said stiffly.

'I'm not Sam,' he said. 'I don't like you being late.'

'Oh, for heaven's sake, Mike!' I said, exasperated. 'Can't you be reasonable? Don't let's have a row in front of Sam and Jude, please.'

'I'm not having a row,' he said stubbornly. 'I'm just telling you what I think.'

'All right,' I sighed, resisting with some difficulty the

53

urge to clobber him.

I don't know what got into him that night. It was really awful. I felt really ashamed at being with him, and apologized to Judy the next day when I saw her after work. We were supposed to be going to see the bed-sit again, just to make sure we really wanted it.

'Though if we don't like it it's tough, seeing we've already paid for it!' I said.

'It'll be all right,' said Judy. 'But about Mike – don't apologize. It's not your fault he's like that. And it's only since you've been leaving home.'

'There you are, it's my parents' fault!' I exclaimed, not really meaning it, but Judy answered seriously.

'No, it's his own fault,' she insisted. 'Sorry, Sue, but I've always felt he was a bit possessive.'

'Oh, well, could be worse,' I said lightly, not knowing whether to be angry at her criticism of my boy-friend, or worried at the implications of what she said. 'Nobody's perfect.'

'Too true,' sighed Judy. 'Except us, of course. Oh, dear, Sue, you'll never believe this but I'm nervous.'

'Nervous? What about?'

'Going into this place, pretending it's mine.'

'It is yours. Ours, anyway.'

'I know, but I don't really believe it. I can't believe I'll be coming here instead of going home to a cosy fire and cups of tea waved in my face, and Mum trying to find out what I've been up to and me trying just as hard not to tell her.'

'You get *fires*, and *tea*?' I said. 'This is a new slant on the old Jude I used to know and love. I hope you're not expecting . . . and what do you mean, fires? It's only September.'

'Only? There was a decided nip in the air this morning. I made for my winter woollies.'

'Jude,' I said solemnly, 'there are things I'm not sure I'm going to like finding out about you.'

'Ditto,' she said cheerfully. We had arrived outside the door of our new home-to-be. 'Will you ring or will I?'

'Do you think they'll mind?' I said nervously.

'What do we want?' she said. 'We obviously don't need to measure for curtains.'

I giggled. 'Nor carpets.'

'Whatever we need, they've got,' said Judy. 'I simply can't think of a good excuse.'

'You can't just go and say, "I want another look in case I've changed my mind",' I agreed.

'When all we really want is a good snoop,' said Judy, 'and it does sound so silly when it's really ours, and we only can't get in because he hasn't give us a key because we said we weren't moving till next week.'

'I think,' I said, 'that we've made a terrible mistake coming here, don't you?'

'Yes,' said Judy decidedly.

So we walked away, feeling fools.

'You didn't?' said Chris when we walked in and put the kettle on for coffee to soothe our shattered nerves. 'You're both utterly and completely cracked.'

'Yeah, we know,' I said, 'but you'd probably have done the same.'

'No, I wouldn't,' she said, 'and I want to see this

place of yours. Tell you what, if you can't face going to look at your own flat on your own, why don't you take me with you and pretend you want to show me?'

We both looked at Chris and said, 'Right!'

'I notice you don't ask me,' said Mum, pretending to be hurt as she added a mug to the row and spooned Nescafé for herself into it.

'You?' I said with derision. 'It's all your fault we're having to go and look this flat in the face. Of course we're not taking you. We're independent.'

'Ha ha,' said Mum hollowly. 'You know . . . ' being serious suddenly, 'now that you've actually found somewhere . . . '

'Yes?'

'I think I'm going to miss you. Very much.'

'You daft thing,' I said, giving her a rough hug because she could talk herself into tears if you let her. 'You'll be round every day, bringing cakes and eggs and offering to do the mending.'

'You must be joking,' said Mum, and poured boiling water into the mugs.

'And that's another thing,' I said. 'We'll get decent coffee with not-boiling water and tea with *very* boiling water instead of the other way round, like you do it!'

She laughed and handed round mugs. 'If you want a servant you have to put up with things done the way the servant does them.' Then she gave another little laugh and said, 'There are times when I wish that it was possible to send one's youngest out into the world instead of the ones that can safely be left behind without a babysitter.'

'Ah, you're regretting it now,' I teased.

'Still, I can always call on you to babysit,' she laughed. 'A swap for letting you use the washing machine, perhaps?'

That was a bit too near the knuckle for comfort, and we changed the subject quickly.

Chapter 5

Well, if Mike wasn't going to be there, helping me move in with Judy, then I felt I didn't want anyone else. It got Mum and Dad a bit upset when I said I didn't want a lift round with my stuff.

'What for?' I said impatiently, still aching inside because of Mike. 'There's nothing much to take. I've packed all the clothes I'll need for a fortnight, and then there's just my duvet and sheets and things. I can come back for them. It's only ten minutes' walk.'

'Not even a lift round in the car?' said Dad with raised eyebrows.

'Well . . . ' I hesitated.

'It's all right, we won't come in. We don't want to know what it looked like before you made it even more hideous.'

Suddenly I laughed. It might well have been the nearly-best bed-sit in the area, but that didn't mean it was furnished with any more care than the rest had been, not in the way of looks anyway.

'It's *incredibly* hideous!' I told him. 'But at least then we won't care if the furniture gets knocked about or people spill red wine on the carpet!'

'That's not the attitude,' he said, with such severity in his voice that for a moment I thought he was serious. 'I hope you're not going to make this place into some kind of gambling hall, or den of vice.'

'Anyway, what does it matter to you what I do there?' I said. 'I thought that was the idea, to let me see what it was like on my own.'

'So long as you bring some of the profits home to us,' he said gravely.

'Eric!' protested my mother, and slapped him on the arm. 'Stop giving the girl ideas.'

'Me?' he said. 'I don't need to give her ideas – she gets them herself.'

'Yeah, I'd like a lift, then,' I said. I wanted to get going, to move in, to get used to the place.

'Sure you don't need anything else?' said Mum.

'Oh, Mum, you were the one that said I wouldn't need anything except my bedclothes. If I do I can always come back, can't I?'

It was funny how our attitudes had changed, I thought, as we drove silently through the few streets to the Victorian house which was to be my – Judy's and my – home from now on. First of all they wanted me to go. Now they're all reluctant and I can't wait.

Judy and her parents were waiting as we arrived.

'Thought you were never coming,' she grumbled as I opened the car door and rushed out, dragging my case with me. 'I felt a right idiot sitting here with Mum and Dad, and they've gone on and on about whether they've done the right thing until I nearly went back home for ever!'

'Why the heck didn't you go in, then?' I said.

'Well – I thought it would be nicer if we both . . . '

I grinned at her. I would have done exactly the same.

'Come on, then. Got the key?'

'I had it under my pillow all night.'

'Then stick it in the lock!'

We left our parents standing on the kerb, being polite to each other, and rushed like kids to the door at the side of the house which was our own, our very own, private entrance. The fact that we had to share a bathroom didn't worry us one bit: it was that front door that was so marvellous.

But the furniture was dreadful!

As our parents crowded in the doorway, they looked, as I felt, decidedly sheepish.

'Don't wait,' I said to mine. 'I'll come back if I really have forgotten anything.'

'At least you're within walking distance,' said my Mum.

'But no telephone . . . ' fretted Judy's.

'Honestly, don't wait, Mum,' said Judy. 'We'll invite you to a meal next weekend, okay? Once we've discovered how the cooker works.'

'Oh, dear, you are going to be all right, aren't you?' twittered her Mum.

Mistake number one, I thought drily. We'll have to be a lot more careful of what we say in their hearing.

'I'll give you a ring from work tomorrow to tell you how we've got on,' said Judy, and I looked at her with admiration. She seemed to be organizing her parents far better than I was.

'Don't you even want us to . . . ' began my Mother.

I took a leaf from Judy's book. 'No, it's all right, really. We'd rather move in on our own.'

Dad brushed a kiss on my cheek and went out, taking Mum's elbow as he went.

We did wave goodbye from the pavement, but it was only a token, really. As soon as the cars had got started up, we were back inside.

'Right,' I said, 'this is my contribution.' And with a flourish I brought out the things that mattered from my roll of bedding. All my favourite posters that I was damned if I was going to leave behind for anyone, particularly Jenny.

'Oh, great,' said Judy. 'I've always fancied that poster myself – can it go where we can both see it?'

'Hang it where you like,' I said generously. 'You're the artistic one. I hereby bequeath you the lot, to hang where you see fit. And,' I said proudly, 'I even remembered a box of drawing pins.'

'Thanks. In that case, what do you think of this?' And she opened one of her cases. Out flowed a dream of gorgeous coloured silks and tapestries, like a river of jewels in that rather drab room.

'For God's sake!' I said, standing with another pock-marked poster in my hand, its corners punctured by many drawing pins.

'You don't think they're too bright?' she said anxiously. 'I mean, if you can't live with them . . . '

'They are *incredible*,' I said. 'Fantastic. Where did you get them?'

'Various places,' she said. 'Markets, prezzies from

people, bits of remnants I thought I might make clothes with and then didn't. I thought we could drape some over this repulsive furniture, if you didn't mind.'

'Mind?' I said. 'That's a touch of genius, Jude. Makes my posters look a bit sick, in fact. Get draping, and we'll see.'

The room was quite big, which made up for the smallness of the kitchen which was about the size of a cupboard. There was a sink and an ancient-looking cooker. Then there was a funny little passage which led to the loo. Our very own. The fact that we had to share the bathroom didn't matter at all.

It was like having someone to stay. We had a friendly fight first about who was going to have which bed.

'*Why*,' asked Judy in affronted tones, 'do they set out the beds so much like beds in bedrooms? I mean to say, it's just *asking* for trouble. No wonder my Mother said "No young men after eleven o'clock".'

I was charmed. 'She didn't, did she? In those exact words?'

'Those exact words,' said Judy solemnly. 'I sometimes wonder whether my parents were born in the reign of George the whatever it was, or Victoria.'

'I don't remember her ever talking about "young men" I must say,' I said, 'not in all the years I've known your Mum.'

But Judy was perfectly sure that she really had said that, and we began a discussion about where she might have got it from – Agatha Christie, perhaps, or the sort of books my parents used to read when they were young: Biggles, and all that.

'If it's okay by you, I'd like this bed,' said Judy,

indicating the one we were sitting on. 'It has character.'

'You mean lumps?' I said.

'I think I could get friendly with these lumps,' she said. 'Is that okay?'

I tested out the other bed. It felt exactly the same to me. Lumpy. 'Okay. Mum said I could exchange it for my own bed if it was too terrible – so long as the landlord takes away this one. She was having kittens about whether I'd get my beauty sleep.'

'Should have heard mine,' said Judy tersely. 'Tell you what, I'll make some coffee then we can decide where to put them.'

'I've already decided,' I said. 'Since you had first choice of lumpy mattress, I'll have first choice of draughts, and I want the window. I like fresh air hurtling down my back. Then we could use it for a sort of window seat in the day time.'

'Great idea,' said Judy, 'and since I don't like fresh air *at all* I'm going where the dregs of the fire will be, and we can use *mine* to sit on in the winter.'

'Like now,' I shivered.

'Now, Sue, we've got to be tough. This electric fire will *eat* money. Blankets and hot water bottles from now on.'

'I don't know why your Mother worried about you,' I said resentfully. 'It was me that was quite happy in slothful comfort at home, and your Mum that didn't think you could cope without it.'

'I've been working it all out for years,' said Judy seriously. 'I've had all the arguments ready: and used them, each time – not that they made a lot of difference till your Mum and Dad did their bit.'

I went to find the biscuits we had packed in our box of essential groceries, while Judy switched on the kettle that was provided, feeling its sides from time to time to see whether it really worked.

'Let's move them now,' I said, opening the packet and throwing a biscuit across to Judy, half-hidden by the kitchen door. 'If we wait till we've had coffee we'll never do it, and I want to know what the room's going to look like.'

The beds were quite easy to move, especially with two of us hauling at them, and by the time we'd shifted them to where we wanted them and then shoved the two chintzy armchairs to better positions the room looked more like a living-space than a bedroom.

'And the table over there, do you think?' said Judy. 'I really like things out of the way, along walls, so that there's space in the middle. I get a bit claustrophobic with tables and things all over the floor so that you trip over them. My Mum's sitting room drives me mad!'

'And then we can put those chairs against it, and just pull them out when we want to eat. Why three, I wonder? I'd have thought two if the landlord was being really mean, or four if he wanted to give us enough for visitors. But three . . . '

'They're the ones he had left over and had to chuck out,' said Judy, with probably more accuracy than she realized. 'Here you are. Are we going to buy milk, or will powdered stuff do?'

'I hadn't *thought* of things like that. Do we want to have some delivered or something? What about break-fast?'

'You don't eat *breakfast*?' said Judy in horrified tones.

'Of course I eat breakfast. I couldn't survive. And I won't get up in time to cook . . . '

'*Cook*? I should hope not. The thought of frying – when you get up – '

'Okay, keep your hair on. Cornflakes, then.'

It was quite a revelation to find out so soon that we were different in odd little ways. Not that it mattered at all – it just seemed funny. And we were enough alike in that we enjoyed putting up our posters and discussing which of Judy's draperies to put where.

'That gorgeous shawl on the table,' I said. 'It will look absolutely marvellous with the tassels hanging down.'

'So long as we move it when anybody comes round,' said Judy. 'I know what would happen – they'd stick their drippy coffee mugs on it and I'd never get the stains out.'

I unrolled my Elvis Presley poster, the one with the most pin-marks in the corners, as I'd had it since I was about six and it had been shifted from wall to wall in my bedroom, and generally bumped into and pulled off and re-pinned a million times.

'No, Sue,' said Judy with emphasis. 'Anything else, but not that.'

'Not my lovely Elvis?' I said, affronted. 'What's wrong with him?'

'I just can't bear him, that's all,' she said simply. 'I couldn't have him looking at me all day. Put him in the loo, if you must, then I won't stay there too long.'

'Tell you what,' I said, 'if I can have this half of the

64

wardrobe I'll put him inside the door so that when I open it I can look. And if I really desperately want to see him when I'm in bed, I can open the door and you can't see from there. It might even stop you taking too long choosing your clothes in the morning.'

It was getting late by the time we'd finished and had the place pretty well as we wanted it. But tired as we were, we didn't seem to want to go to bed. We sat on Judy's – with the fire on – 'Just this once, since we're new to things' – and felt a bit silly saying, 'Well, suppose we'd better . . . '

And of course it didn't matter because it was Sunday tomorrow and it wasn't one of my Sundays on so even I didn't have to get up. There was no pressure at all, nobody to look at their watches and give meaningful glances. There wasn't even that quiet tenseness about a house where everyone else had gone to bed and you haven't and it sort of *matters*.

We did move eventually, of course, taking turns to clean our teeth in our very own kitchen sink, and then taking more turns to make more and more coffee until we had to start taking it in turns to go along the cold passage to our very own loo. And then of course we went on with the conversation from opposite ends of our room, until the spaces between replies lengthened and I awoke, chilled, at something like four o'clock in the morning to find the central light blazing, and had to pad out of bed, find the switch and turn it off.

Judy was a hump and a fringe of blonde hair when I awoke properly at about eleven, the sun shining hotly through the curtains beside me.

I didn't feel in the least odd, or wonder where I was, as I had expected. But it was nice, just for a few moments, to cuddle the room to myself and feel it was all mine, to do with as I liked, and live in for as long as I wanted.

There was a tiny streak of regret in me that I *wasn't* on my own. I had a strange feeling inside that I didn't know whether I was going to get on with living with someone else. I hadn't even shared a bedroom for ten years, let alone a whole existence.

But those feelings didn't last long. This was a new departure in my life. I was eighteen, independent, my own woman.

'Do you want a cup of tea?'

I won't print the words that emerged from Judy's bed, but they were enough to convince me that what she said about not being very good in the mornings was absolutely true! So I made my own cup of tea and breakfast and left Judy to go back to sleep. Which she did with no effort at all.

Mike and Sam were coming round for the very first time this evening, and I wasn't looking forward to it. It was also going to be the very last time I'd see Mike for a while because he was going off to college on Monday morning.

I couldn't get out of my head all those hints that he wanted me to be a little wife rushing forward with the pipe and slippers. To be honest, I was a bit scared of him saying anything more plainly, and yet I knew he'd be annoyed that Sam and Jude would be there as well. I'd have preferred a lovely romantic evening, too, but I knew it wouldn't be like that at all – there'd be more moans and lectures.

'It's funny, you know,' I said to Judy some hours later after she'd got up and was energetically searching through the useful recipe book a mutual friend had bought for us to see what we would eat this evening that wasn't baked beans or bread.

Judy grunted, and I thought it was because she was concentrating on sausage and mash, but then she turned and said, 'He's still not happy about it, then?'

'You're telling me,' I said. 'I wish we'd had a bit more time for him to get used to me being here.'

Then Judy started to laugh. 'It's just as well you're going to be around all the time, in fact, then Sam won't be tempted to stay and my Mother won't worry her little socks off.'

'How's she going to know?' I asked.

'I don't know, but I'm always sure she's going to. I suppose I haven't grown out of Mummy yet. Give us time!'

'You know,' I said, after approving Judy's choice of meal, 'if they didn't go on about sex so much you wouldn't be nearly as likely to want to try it out.'

'Who? Parents? Oh, God, yes. I've had enough warning about having boys around here to last a hundred years.'

'In fact you feel like getting pregnant on purpose just because it's what they're expecting,' I said, wishing I'd taken the potato peeler from home because if I used the blunt instrument provided by our landlord there wouldn't be much potato left to cook. 'Listen, shall I just scrub these?'

'I dunno,' said Judy. 'Isn't the peel poisonous?'

'What about jacket potatoes, you prannock?'

'Oh, I suppose – okay, then. Yes. I like jacket potatoes. Hell, is that the time? I wanted to have this lot all doing nicely so that I had masses of time to put my make-up on, so that they don't think we're incompetent.'

'We are,' I said. 'There, that's the last spud. If they don't like the skin on they can just put up with it. Tell you what, you go and throw your make-up on and I'll slosh things around to make a sauce for this. Thank God for pressure cookers. I'm glad your Mum was throwing this out.'

'*Why* was she throwing it out, that's what I want to know,' said Judy darkly. 'Still, if it explodes there will at least be two able bodied macho men to clear up the mess.'

'Don't make me laugh,' I said. 'Clearing up explosions is women's work, didn't you know? Talking of macho muscles – you know that new bloke that's part time at the shop? He's got muscles that he can ripple all up and down his arm, but ask him to carry a crate of milk up from the cellar and it's a different matter!'

The boys were about ten minutes late, which was a good thing, because by then we'd got the table ready (Judy's beautiful shawl removed and hidden in case of accidents) and an easy chair moved over so that someone could sit on the arm, and Judy had all her make-up on. I nearly forgot about mine, till Judy handed the mirror over. But since they were a few minutes late I even had time for my eye-shadow.

And Mike waved a couple of bottles of bubbly when they arrived, which I thought was really nice of him. I immediately took back all those nasty things which I'd been saying, both mentally and to Judy. And the Almost cordon bleu sausage and jacket potato tasted better than I (or Judy) expected, so the boys were genuine in their praises. (The sauce had been a complete disaster. Its horrible remains were the first item in our bin under the sink.)

It was a great evening. And then Mike and Sam began to make going-home noises, and we were all four of us standing awkwardly by our own private front door. The new flat – sorry, bed-sit – was nicely paved right up to the door, with no useful screen of bushes or trees or anything. A bit stark, in fact.

'Er – want to come for a short walk before I go?' said Mike.

I didn't. I was tired. I was exhausted. I'd had just enough fizzy wine to make me sleepy but not enough to throw sense to the winds and say, 'Bother work tomorrow, he's going away.'

He was going away tomorrow, and I wasn't prepared to 'go for a walk' to say goodbye.

'Sure,' I said, stifling a yawn. 'I'll get a jumper. And a key.'

We wandered down the path and onto the main road, then round the corner to the bridge over the canal before Mike spoke.

'She might have gone and let us stay there,' he complained.

'What do you mean?'

'Our last night, and all that. I'd have thought she'd have more tact. And Sam. As it is, there she is with Sam, on her own . . . '

'Don't be silly, Mike,' I snapped, 'Sam will have gone by now.'

'You're being naïve,' he sneered. 'What do you think he was hanging about for? Just waiting for me to get out of the way, that's what. And now I won't have a turn because I won't be here.'

'A turn? For Godsake, Mike, what are you hinting at?' though I realized with a thundering heart exactly what he did mean. And knew that I didn't want him to mean anything like that at all.

'You know,' he said hoarsely, and pulled me into the trees at the beginning of the steps down to the towpath.

'Don't, Mike,' I said, trying to detach myself.

'Don't? Why not? How long have we been going out together? Sue, I'm going away tomorrow. This is the last chance . . . '

'The last *what*?'

'I don't have to spell it out, do I?'

'Yes,' I said bluntly.

'Oh, come on, Sue, you know what I'm getting at,' and his mouth came clamping down on mine so that I could hardly breathe. I struggled and pushed him away. 'Mike! Stop!'

'Why stop?' he insisted. 'I don't want to stop. Look, it's fairly dry down here, if I take my jacket off and . . . '

'Mike, I don't *want* to!' I tried to make it as emphatic as I could, and I was really beginning to get scared. Because although those macho muscles are mostly for show, they were damned useful for a bloke to overpower a girl if he wanted to.

His hands were all over me, undoing buttons I didn't want undone. He laughed as I wrestled with him, and I really think he thought I wanted him to hurl me to the ground and make love exactly where we were, only yards from the road.

But eventually I must have convinced him.

'Okay, not here,' he said, pulling away and taking my arm instead to pull me further into the enveloping trees. 'We'll walk a bit further, shall we?'

'I don't think you understand, Mike,' I said, trying to keep my voice steady but not succeeding very well. 'I don't want to. At all. Not anywhere.'

'Don't keep telling me I don't understand!' he said violently, then was silent while he dragged me further into what seemed impenetrable jungle in the darkness. 'But I thought that was why you wanted a flat . . . why you agreed with your parents . . . '

'No!' I cried. 'How could you think that? It wasn't my idea at all, in fact it was only you being against it that made me realize what a good idea it was!'

I shouldn't have said that. His anger made him grip me tighter then ever as we came to a stop near some huge pink blossoms of balsam, rising higher than us in the damp verges of the canal and lit by the curtained windows of a house whose garden snuggled on the opposite bank. Mike seemed to have changed so much: or was it that I saw him in a different light now?

'Mike,' I said, more gently now, '*please* . . . '

He didn't pretend to misunderstand this time. He dropped his arm down and said in a defeated voice, 'Okay, then, if that's really how you want it.'

I wanted to say all kinds of things. I wanted to tell

him that I loved him. I wanted to tell him that I didn't want this kind of panic-grab-at-the-next-opportunity thing because my kind of loving wasn't a need for sex grabbed behind a tree by the canal. I wanted to explain that I liked being with him, and I liked him kissing me, but that was all I wanted at the moment. I wanted to tell him about my plans for the future – those plans which weren't, probably, going to include him.

Instead I said, 'That's how I want it. Sorry.'

He didn't say anything on the way back; he didn't hold my hand, or arm, or anything. Several times I drew in breath to say something. Several times I opened my mouth. But each time I knew this wasn't the right time, and anyway, I didn't know whether he'd want to listen.

For people who were supposed to be in love, and seeing each other for the last time for ages, we were behaving pretty strangely.

'Well – see you sometime, I suppose,' said Mike at the flat door.

My heart was aching.

'I'll write,' I said. 'Will you write back?'

'Well, I can't phone you,' he said, making it into a complaint. 'Unless you're back at your parents. You can tell me when that happens.'

'If,' I corrected him.

'I don't suppose it will be long,' he said. And then my last feeling of guilt that I hadn't given my love what he wanted melted away.

'I think it's most unlikely,' I said coldly.

And that was how we parted.

Chapter 6

I missed him. I missed him horribly.

As my period started the next day I thought my feelings by the canal must have been PMT or something like that – nothing to do with anything Mike had said or done.

'You all right, Sue?' said Judy a week or two later. 'You look a bit down.'

'I'm all right,' I said. 'Just a bit cheesed off, that's all. Fed up with working days other people don't. I'm fed up with this work anyway. Chuck over the local paper. I'll see if there are any better jobs going.'

'There aren't,' said Judy flatly. 'I've already looked.'

'You too?' I said.

'I haven't got enough O levels to get promoted,' she said. 'And if I wanted to go really high up in the bank I'd need A's anyway. Still, I suppose we're bloody lucky to have jobs at all, considering what it's like round here.'

'Don't rub it in,' I said. 'You'll be like Mike next, going on about women taking all the jobs men ought to have and creating unemployment and really we ought to sit at home and do our knitting.'

Judy laughed. 'No, not really. I was just trying to convince myself I don't really need O levels, that's all. Did Mike really say that?'

'Near as dammit,' I said, feeling unreasonably angry with him for going away. If he hadn't been at college, I thought, I shouldn't be sitting here feeling brainless and a fool for working instead of sitting happily at home where I'd be looked after until I got married.

I'd so much talked myself into wanting to be in this flat that I'd forgotten it wasn't my idea but my parents', and that I couldn't have sat around waiting to get married even if I wanted to, which of course I didn't.

But I was finding sharing this flat very, very difficult, and I missed my Mum and Dad – and even Chris and Jenny! Sometimes I just wanted to be looked after at home. Don't ever share a flat with your best friend! There are secrets which people should be allowed to keep in the privacy of their own homes.

I became more and more irritated by the way you had to get Judy out of bed with a crowbar in the mornings. I nearly didn't bother, but somehow I felt responsible for getting her off to work, as if I was her Mother! And Judy didn't seem even to try to get up by herself.

'If you went to bed earlier you'd be able to get up in the morning,' I groused one evening when she was getting ready to go out with Sam.

'You're quite wrong, you know,' said Judy, wrinkling her nose at her reflection in our only mirror. 'I wouldn't be able to get up even if I went to bed at nine o'clock for a fortnight.'

'Well,' was all I could think of to reply. The truth was, I was miserably jealous. It was all very well Judy going out with Sam every night, and if Mike was here I'd probably do exactly the same. It would have been really great to be able to come home whenever I liked and not wonder if Mum or Dad were worrying . . . So I suppose in some ways I could sympathize with Judy, revelling in her new freedom. I'd had more of it than she had, anyway.

Only Mike wasn't here, and I had to stay in the flat, all on my own, every wretched night. *And* get her up in the mornings. That really got on my nerves.

Anyway, one evening I was feeling even rattier than usual. I'd had a rotten day at work. Sadie had been sadistic. I'd wanted to talk it out with Judy. I mean, what's the point of living with your best friend if she's not there to talk to when you need her? We'd arranged to stay in that evening and move the furniture about, now that we'd finally decided where we wanted everything to go. And for once Sam wasn't able to come round as he had to take his aunt to the cinema or something.

Actually today Sadie really had something to moan about, even if it wasn't entirely my fault. I was lugging a crate of milk up from the cellar (it wasn't the part time chap's shift, of course, just when you needed him) because we'd only got two pints left in the shop and the place was empty, for a change. Then someone came in, rather suddenly, and made me jump so I caught my foot in the hole in the lino which I normally take bloody good care to avoid. I lurched forwards, and hurled the crate right into the front of the display fridge. I didn't know what to *do*! And the customer wasn't much help either. She didn't make any attempt to pick anything up – not even me – but said, 'You aren't half going to catch it, aren't you?' and other just as helpful comments, meanwhile looking annoyed that I wasn't jumping out of the mess of smashed glass and milk to serve her.

Well, I got her bread or sweets or whatever it was she wanted, and began to try and do something about the mess.

Then of course people kept coming in, and they all said really stupid things, watching me with the brush and dustpan, shovelling up acres of glass, and none of them even asked if I wanted any help. Honestly all I wanted to do was scream at the whole lot of them then fall in a heap on the floor and cry. Finally I just phoned Harry and told him what had happened, saying ungraciously, 'I suppose you'll knock the damage off my wages,' when he arrived because I was in such a foul temper. I'd probably have been in a lot better mood if I *had* cried.

'Don't worry,' he said. 'We'll get it off the insurance. How did it happen?'

I cheered up a little bit. At least he was a bit more comforting than Sadie would have been. I told him, and all he said was, 'An accident. Could happen to anyone.' Then he busied himself clearing up the remains of the tiny bits of glass which I'd missed – round the edges of the refrigerator itself, for instance, where it hadn't occurred to me to look – and packing up the contents in a cardboard box to take home to his own fridge.

When Sadie arrived she knew all about it, of course. She gave me one long, cold look then marched straight to our tiny staff-room and made a cup of tea. She didn't offer me one.

'I'm sorry,' I said, not meaning the words to come out the way they did. They didn't sound sorry at all, but I'd had a basin full of Sadie's temperament.

She looked at me directly for the first time that day. 'Oh?' she said. That's all. It indicated that whatever I said and however I said it she knew that I'd done the whole thing on purpose just out of spite. And she wouldn't believe I was sorry even if I offered to pay for twenty fridges out of my own money and personally scrubbed the floor ten times to get rid of the last remaining splashes of milk.

So by the time I got home I was in a really foul mood and Judy got the full force of it.

I walked in and there she was, lying on her bed, and the room looking like a pigsty. It was always like a pigsty, and I didn't usually care, and anyway there'd been no point in clearing it up because we were going to shift furniture. But there she was, lounging about again, in the same sort of way as I'd left her this morning, and I just felt so furious and resentful that I laid into her.

'For God's sake, Jude, can't you do *anything*!'

She'd half risen from the bed when I came in. Now she sank back onto it. Her eyes narrowed against the afternoon light as it came through the window.

'Pardon?'

'This – this bloody *mess* in here. Why am I the only one who does anything?'

'I thought we were going to do it together, this evening.' Her voice was dangerously soft, sociable. I should have had more sense.

'*If* you manage to stay in for the evening,' I said, and went for the box by the stove where we'd decided to keep our small stock of cleaning materials. I began rubbing a duster vigorously over the nearest surface, picking up the cups we had left at breakfast time and throwing them so violently into the tiny sink that they ought to have smashed.

'I told you I wasn't out tonight. We agreed to move the furniture around. I'm not working twice,' she said calmly.

'You're just used to having you dear Mother clearing up after you,' I said spitefully and unforgivably, swiping the duster over every surface I could see.

I heard, rather than saw, Judy get slowly off her bed, pull a case from underneath it and snap open the locks. There were noises of drawers opening, and the swish of something that I realized later was embroidered cloth from the table. I dared not look round. I felt so ashamed of myself, and my head was throbbing. But though I'd managed to say 'Sorry', even in an ungracious way, to the hated Sadie this afternoon, I couldn't, simply couldn't, say the same to my best friend at this moment.

I heard the sharp click as the case was shut, and the heavy tread of her shoes crossing the room.

'I'll send you this week's rent,' she said, and opened the door.

That terrifyingly empty voice galvanized me into action. I was able to move.

'Jude . . . '

'I'm not staying here to be talked at like that. I do my share. I'm not doing things simply because you want them done.'

'It was only . . . ' I began, wanting to tell her about my day at work and the broken fridge and Sadie but not seeming able to do it.

'You're "only" too often,' she said. 'I shall go home to my over-indulgent mother. As you probably thought I would. Goodbye.'

'Judy . . .'

And it was too late. I heard her heels go determinedly down the path outside the window where my bed was.

It was probably about an hour later when the door bell went. I don't know exactly. I was too upset and angry with myself to notice.

'Mike!' was my immediate thought, and some of the awfulness lightened. Then I knew how stupid I was. Even if he had wanted to come all that way to see me for an evening he'd have gone to my parents. He wouldn't, I knew Mike, have come to surprise me like that.

More likely my Mother. Or sisters. Or anybody. Not Mike.

By this time I'd reached the door and opened it dully.

'Yes?'

'It's all right, Sue, it's only me.'

Sam.

I opened the door wide. 'Sam! But you're taking an aunt to the dentist or an uncle to a funeral or something.'

'My grandmother to my auntie's, but she decided at the last minute she didn't want to go. Had a row or something.'

'Sorry, Sam, she's not here.'

Sam walked in. So did someone else I'd never seen before in my life.

'Not? Can we come in and wait? This is Paul, by the way.'

'Hello, Paul.'

I'd have to explain. 'I don't think there's much point in waiting.' I began sullenly. 'I think she's gone off to her Mum's.'

'Oh, well, I'd better not go round too, since she hasn't been back home for a while.'

'It's not like that,' I hesitated. 'Oh, God. Want some coffee?'

'What's the matter?' Sam was plainly alarmed. 'Nothing wrong, is there?'

'Not really,' I said. 'Oh, hell, yes. Only it was my fault. We had a row and she went off.'

'Oh dear,' said Sam, not very helpfully. 'I suppose I'd better go round and face the old cow.'

'Don't you call my friend names!' I yelled, feeling more like an eight-year-old than someone of eighteen.

'Not her, her Mum,' explained Sam. 'No, I don't mean it, not really. We get on all right. Only it was better . . . no, I won't have a coffee, thanks, Sue. I'll nip round, see what's going on.'

'I'm sorry,' I said miserably. 'I honestly didn't mean . . .'

I hadn't meant to have a row with her, no, but I shouldn't have expected her to put up with a childish temper like that. I'd have reacted in exactly the same way, only I'd probably have said a lot more. 'Tell her I'm sorry, will you, Sam?'

'What for?' said good-natured Sam, clearly not understanding how really nasty I'd been. 'She'll be all **right**. She always is.'

I sniffed a bit and said I hoped so. Then Sam turned and nodded to Paul, who I'd hardly looked at, and said, 'Sorry, Paul. Want to come too, or will you . . . ?'

'If she's upset,' said Paul, 'you won't want me there. Did you mean it about coffee?' he said to me, giving me a look of such frank admiration that my mouth dropped open and I stood there like an idiot for several seconds. It had been so *long* since anyone had looked at me like that! I was instantly conscious of my dirty work clothes, my old make-up that I'd had on all day and which was almost certainly shiny in the wrong places. 'If you don't mind me being here, not knowing me, that is.'

Mind! How could anybody mind, when someone looked at you like that! Especially someone with those amazing blue eyes. I'd never seen eyes like them – really dark, so that in some lights they looked almost black.

'I could meet you later or something,' he was saying to Sam while my mouth still gaped open like a fish.

Sam was obviously relieved. 'Okay, mate. See you. See you, Sue.'

He went off, and I felt a bit of an idiot with nothing to say, only the remains of a row and an awareness that I hadn't behaved very well behind me and here was this dishy bloke in my flat, all to myself.

Stop that, I told myself sternly as I mumbled platitudes. You're Mike's girl-friend, right?

But Paul sat down easily on one of the chairs we were going to have moved that evening and said, 'What happened?'

'It was just . . . ' I began lamely. But he was different from Mike. I felt as if he really did want to know. Mike would have said the same, and then immediately gone on and talked about something else which interested *him*. And suddenly I wanted to talk, very much. Not just about Judy and me this evening, but about everything else as well. I'd missed talking to somebody. It was worse now that we'd got the bed-sit together. At home there had always been Mum and Dad or Chris. Even Jenny sometimes. But now it was either an empty room or a sleeping room-mate. And tonight I'd been looking forward to telling her all my worries about Mike going away to college and about my job and Sadie and the fridge . . .

I started to tell him, then turned on the tap so fiercely that I almost drowned myself and the tiny kitchen. Paul laughed and came over to help, and I found myself giggling hysterically while we tried to dry me and the floor with my damp face towel.

'That's better,' he said. 'You looked all white and rigid before. Now tell me where the coffee is and I'll make it. About a heaped spoonful for you? More? Less?'

'Perfect,' I said, still exploding into hysterical giggles from time to time as I sat back in the chair and waited for the kettle to boil. 'Sorry, I must seem like a right pillock. It's just that I had this awful day at work, and smashed a fridge, and then this row with Jude . . . I shouldn't be laughing.'

'Better than crying,' commented Paul, standing with his back to me, watching the kettle as it hissed and sang domestically behind the door. 'But go on. You were going to tell me all about it.'

'How do you know Sam?' I hedged.

'We were talking about your problems,' he reminded me. 'Sam says you're Judy's best friend. So what happened?'

'Oh, I'd just had this terrible day at work, and I said something I shouldn't have. That's all.'

The kettle was boiling. He poured water into the mugs, added milk, glanced over with an enquiring look and a spoon poised over the sugar, tipped a spoonful in his own and brought the mugs over before sitting down.

'Yes?'

I can't usually talk to men. I always think they'll be bored if the conversation isn't about beer or football. But he seemed to want to know, and I needed to talk to someone – it was easier with a stranger, too. 'I've never had a row with her before, as far as I can remember,' I said. 'It's only because of this flat – I like it tidy, Jude doesn't care, and I'd crashed into a fridge at work and smashed it up and our manager put my back up because she wasn't a bit helpful or sympathetic. I mean,' I went on, warming to my subject, 'I could really have hurt myself, with all that broken glass.'

I told him all the details, and suddenly it sounded really funny and we were both laughing our heads off about it.

'So you see, by the time I'd got back I was in this foul mood and Jude was lying around and I just wanted someone to mother me and pat me on the head and make me a cup of tea and that, and of course she didn't. Why should she? So I lost my temper and that's it. I was really more upset because it was the one night she wasn't going out with Sam and we were going to do things together . . . '

Then I found myself pouring out all the things about my parents telling me to go, 'and I don't know whether you'll understand this, but though I've got over them chucking me out, and I really do think they did the right thing, and I actually *like* being away from home now, I still can't stop sometimes feeling really miserable about them wanting to get rid of me.'

'It does feel a bit like that, doesn't it?' he said as if he knew. 'Even when you understand exactly why, and how they've done their best for you. You still feel you'd rather have made the decision for yourself.'

'How do you know?' I exclaimed. 'Are you psychic or something?'

'Only the victim of the same kind of parents,' he smiled. 'But it was easier for me — my sister and I got our marching orders at the same time, so we got a flat together. And we squabbled like crazy for the first few months. We seemed to take it in turns to flounce out and go home to Mum!'

I laughed, and for the first time that evening felt at ease. 'I suppose it's my turn next. Probably when Judy gets fed up with me going on about Mike. It must be a bit tedious.'

I could have cut off my tongue! Why mention Mike, for heaven's sake, just when things were going nicely?

And then I felt ashamed again. Of course I had to mention Mike, so that Paul didn't get the wrong idea about me, and when his dark eyebrows rose and he said, 'Mike?' I was able to explain quite naturally,

'He's my boy-friend. He's away at the moment, at college, doing engineering. He wasn't too keen on me having a flat, and said really horrible things about my parents. And then, sort of contrarily, I went against him and did as I was told without a fight. He was really annoyed about it. But by then I'd decided I wanted to have a flat, and didn't want to fight about it at all. Honestly, I've really liked being here, with a friend, on our own. Jude had to persuade her parents to let her share with me, you know.'

'I think Sam said something . . . '

'And I thought it would be really great to share with a friend, instead of being on my own. Only she's not here very much so I haven't got a room-mate at all.' And then I told him about Judy's difficulty getting up in the morning and how the row must have been building up long before this evening when I'd been nasty about having to get her out of bed.

'In fact I was really nasty,' I said, quite cheerfully. Then I sobered again. 'I don't suppose she'll come back.'

'Why not?' said Paul. He'd shifted away from me now, setting his coffee carefully down on the bare table. I found myself, again, treacherously wishing I hadn't mentioned Mike.

'After what I've told you?'

'That's only your opinion. It takes two to quarrel.'

'Wanna bet?' I said. 'I seem to manage it quite well on my own.'

'I'm sure she'll come back,' said Paul. 'Don't keep blaming yourself.' He drained his coffee mug and put it down again. 'Look . . . ' he hesitated.

'Yes?' I took up the mug and began moving across the room towards the kitchen.

'Let's go and do something. You're upset and Sam's taken off and left me on my own. Fancy a movie? There's just time to get in to the main film. Bearing in mind of course that you have a boy-friend, but it would be nice to have someone to go to the movies with.'

It didn't take me long to make up my mind.

'Thanks, Paul,' I said. 'I'd love to.'

Chapter 7

I was full of hope when I arrived home after work the next day, expecting, quite strongly, that Judy would be there as she had been for the last six weeks.

She wasn't.

The nice evening at the cinema with Paul, the half hour's talk afterwards in a pub in town, the bus ride back and the quiet goodnight without touching at the door – all that melted away. I was faced with the reality that I had quarrelled with my best friend and I was on my own.

I felt incredibly lonely. Even more than when Jude was out in the evenings and left me to myself. What was worse, she must have been back sometime while I wasn't there because the rest of her clothes were gone, her sheets had been ripped from her bed and the little pile of books by the gas fire was no longer there.

I cried.

Half an hour later I'd recovered enough to put on a kettle for a coffee and to look into the cupboard for something to eat. It might cheer me up, I thought — mistakenly, because when I opened the cupboard there were all the things we'd put there together and I didn't know whether I ought to have half a tin of soup in case Judy ever returned to eat the other half, whether I should add up what there was and divide by two and send the money to her, whether I should merely separate what I knew to be hers and wait for her to come back and claim her property.

I just didn't know what to do.

And then I got angry that she'd left her bed with all the landlord's blankets trailing on the floor, as if she'd done it deliberately because I'd moaned about her not doing anything for the flat. Then I started throwing anything of hers I could find around the room.

It made me feel a whole lot better: there's nothing like throwing things around to get rid of your frustrations!

Then I tidied up and put all of Judy's things into a cardboard box.

I started to laugh. My temper had gone. I felt really silly picking things up like that as if we'd had a divorce or something! For heaven's *sake* I told myself, you've only been sharing with a friend. Your friend doesn't want to share any more, that's all. Nothing to get into a state about. And you don't have to pack her things up. She can jolly well come and pack her own things up if she wants to.

So I put them all back again.

Okay, you're thinking, 'That Sue, a bit of a nut case. Wouldn't catch me behaving like that.' No. You probably wouldn't. You'd do the sensible thing and go home to *your* Mum.

I still hung on to Paul's conviction that she'd be back and that I could have another go at trying to get on with people.

Maybe it was just that Judy and I, though good friends in the normal way, just weren't the type of people to get on well stuck together in one room. No wonder she'd gone out with Sam every night.

I didn't really know whether I could afford it on my own.

I blamed Mike for going away. It was all his fault. If he'd been around, I could have gone out with him sometimes, or he could have come to the flat sometimes. Either way I'd have had company. And sometimes Judy and I could have said to both our boyfriends, 'We don't want you round tonight – hen evening,' or something like that.

Great when you can organize your life and other people's in your imagination! It's a pity it doesn't work like that in real life. I realized that real life was a mixture of mistaken ideas, even more mistaken actions, second bests and accidents.

Even Paul hadn't said anything about seeing me again.

That thought came into my mind without my noticing it. You see what I mean? I didn't intend it at all – I didn't want to be disloyal to Mike – yet here I was wishing this nice, friendly, good-looking guy would come and take me out again! And I found myself daydreaming about him as well – he was so different from Mike. Where Mike was stocky and muscular, Paul was tall and slim. Mike's hair was a sort of mouse brown, never tidy, but standing up in a kind of haystack above his broad forehead. Paul had closely cropped dark hair, incredibly well styled (I made a mental note to ask who cut his hair) and where Mike's clothes were neat, against Paul's they looked as if he'd taken them out of a drawer with his eyes shut and put them on without caring about colour matching or anything. Not that this meant Mike was a scruff, or that Paul was any kind of pansy. They just happened to look like that.

I stopped myself. I was being horribly disloyal to Mike. I was mentally comparing him with Paul, criticizing all the things I'd loved. And I'd only written to him a couple of days ago, telling him how much I missed him and how much I needed him and wanted him to come back.

It was quite true. I did want him to come back. And that was probably just why I was daydreaming about Paul, who had been nice to me one evening. Serve him right, though, I thought, if I did go out with someone else. He should have written every day, sent me roses, refused to go to his college if it meant leaving me . . .

Ha ha. Some hopes. Romance like that wasn't built Mike's way.

Still, there was no reason why I shouldn't *dream* of romance like that, especially as there wasn't anything in it.

What else was there to do, after all, in a bed-sitter by yourself?

But when Paul turned up a couple of hours later, I honestly thought for a moment that I must have made it happen just by thinking. My mind was a guilty whirl of surprise and pleasure. I don't think he noticed. I hope he didn't. His first words were perfectly ordinary, just what I should have expected if I'd dreamed the right dreams, and not those which I shouldn't have dreamed if I was truly in love with Mike.

'Has she come back?'

I had to rethink everything. Had who come back? For heaven's sake, Sue, he's talking about *Jude!*

I shook my head mutely, working out what I was supposed to do with him now. The memory of my daydreams made me blush.

'I'm sure she will,' he said comfortingly. 'It's early days yet. I haven't seen Sam yet, so I thought I'd pop round to check.'

'That's nice of you,' I said. I made a special effort to be loyal to my boy-friend, not to let myself get carried away by the fascinating smile and the deep blue eyes of Paul. 'I was just about to write to Mike about it.'

'Sounds a good idea,' approved Paul, and the attracted part of me wanted to kick myself for pushing the idea of Mike in front of him, while the loyal part felt all smug.

All the same, it was really nice to feel he wanted to come round and see me, especially when he said lightly, 'I don't suppose you'll feel like cooking on your own, so how about coming out for a pizza or something? If you haven't eaten already, that is.'

'You must be joking!' I said feelingly. 'One of the things Jude and I do best is *not* cook. I've been trying to decide for the last two hours whether I really wanted the same can of soup today *and* tomorrow, or whether I should give up and run home to Mum myself.'

'You wouldn't give up that easily,' said Paul with conviction. 'That's settled then. Let's go.'

'I have to point out, though . . . ' I began.

'That you're skint and until your rich uncle in Australia dies you won't be unskint till next week?' Paul asked.

'Something like that,' I agreed.

'Good thing my rich uncle died *last* week, then, isn't it?' he said. 'Tell you what, I'll buy you a pizza today, and you can do me baked beans tomorrow. Okay?'

If I hadn't taken a good grip on myself I could easily have fallen for that one. He was going too fast. There was Mike. I had to remember there was Mike. If I wanted him to be true to me, I couldn't go out with just anyone I fancied on the spur of the moment myself. Suppose, I asked myself, suppose Mike took a girl out to eat? How would I feel?

I knew exactly how I would feel.

'Sorry, Paul, but I think I won't, after all. Sorry. The thought of it was very nice, but . . . '

'But there's Mike,' said Paul easily. 'Sure. I know. I'm taking advantage of you being lonely. Sorry. I'll pop in again tomorrow, see that you're okay. Bye for now.'

Had I made the most stupid decision of my whole life? I listened to his springing footsteps down the path

91

and wanted desperately to call him back. I had to make myself think again how I'd feel if Mike did this to me.

If only he'd write to me, I said angrily to myself, I wouldn't get myself into situations where I'd be attracted to anyone else. He'd been gone ages – six weeks, at least. I didn't want to work out the actual dates in case it was longer and I felt even more ill-used. But I did work out that even if things were new and exciting, even if he'd had problems with the digs he'd found and wanted to move out to different ones, even if he found the work a bit more than he expected, surely in six weeks he'd have found the odd five minutes to scribble a postcard.

Even if he was still refusing to accept the fact that I'd moved away from home.

I'd written tons to him. At least (I mentally counted up) seven so far, which was an average of one a week. I'd told him how I felt and how Judy and I were getting on and lots of little things about work and all that. But mostly it was about how much I loved him and missed him.

Well, I'd told Paul I was just going to write about Jude's and my row, so to make the lie true I'd better do just that, to stop myself cursing the fact that I hadn't had anything to eat and what I'd really like most in the world at this moment would be a deep pan chilli pizza!

Judy wasn't there when I came home from work the next day either. Nothing had been moved. Nothing had changed.

Except me.

I'd decided, finally decided, that I'd had enough of

Sadie and the shop. I said to myself if Mike could go off to college, so could I. If my parents thought I could do better than work in a shop, then I could. If I couldn't share a flat with someone without messing things up because I was unhappy at work, then it was time I did something about it.

So did I. I gave Sadie my notice.

I wished, really wished, that Judy was here so that I could tell her what Sadie's face looked like. Later on, when I'd had something to eat, I'd go to my parents and tell them, but it wouldn't be as much fun, because they'd be worried about me paying rent out of dole money. And without Jude to help. Oh God, and I'd have to tell them about that as well.

I began talking to myself — it gets you quickly, madness, when you're on your own!

'You should have seen her, Jude,' I said solemnly to the teapot. 'Her face went about ten shades of purple, all at once.'

I imagined Judy so well that when I heard the key scrape in the lock I wasn't altogether surprised. And when she walked in through the door I said, as naturally as if nothing had happened, 'I'm trying to think of a better word than purple to describe Sadie's face.'

She came in shyly, sort of creeping, if you see what I mean? Not like Jude, who slams her way in anywhere unless it's early morning when she sleeps her way in.

'What?' Even her voice wasn't like Jude's. You won't believe it but I'd actually forgotten, completely, for a few minutes that she'd walked out on me a couple of days ago.

'Sadie. Oh, sorry, I was telling you only you didn't

93

happen to be here at the time. I've given in my notice.'

Her face broke into a smile – the real smile of the Judy that I knew. 'You haven't. Honestly? Crikey, Sue, have you come into a million or something? Or got another job?'

Gleefully I began to tell her about the argument I'd had with Sadie . . . 'It was all because of that damned fridge,' I said.

'What fridge?' Judy interrupted.

'I told you – didn't I?'

'*What* fridge?' she repeated.

'Well, I was carrying this crate of milk up from the cellar and someone came into the shop and made me jump . . .'

I told the whole story all over again, and then told her the latest instalment today.

'Anyway, Sadie and I got into a bit of an argument and I thought, "Sue, why don't you get out of this if you really hate it?" so I did.'

'Did what?'

'Gave in my notice,' I said simply, wondering why I hadn't told Paul about it. Paul, again! I must keep my mind off Paul. 'I've got a week,' I said. 'Then I'm free.'

'You didn't!' said Judy.

'I feel fantastic. So far.'

'When did all this happen?' she said. 'About the fridge, I mean. I don't remember you telling me.'

'On, ar – um – er – it was the day before yesterday.'

'Ah,' said Judy. 'I see.'

'Well, I would have told you later.'

'Only I walked out.'

'Yeah. I don't really blame you. I was in a bit of a bad temper.'

'I can see why,' said Judy ruefully. 'I'm – like – sorry, Sue. Honest. I was a bit miffed at something and, well, you know . . .'

'That's all right.'

'I brought my sheets back.'

'Hell, I made the bed,' I said, joking. 'I'd have left it if I'd known you were coming back before it annoyed me.'

'I'll still have to undo it,' said Judy. 'I'm damned if I'm sleeping on raw blanket. But to go back to you giving in your notice – what are you going to do? I mean, are we going to be able to go on affording this?'

'What a cheek!' I said. 'You didn't mind about *me* affording it when you waltzed off!'

'I wasn't going to waltz off for ever,' said Judy impatiently. 'You should have known that.'

I didn't say anything. I couldn't have told her about my misery over those two days.

'The DHSS will fork out for it, I hope,' I said confidently. 'I'll go and see them tomorrow. Plenty of time now. I might go and find me an evening job as well. Karen said they wanted part time staff at the Mitre. I rather fancy being a barmaid.'

Judy slipped off her shoes and dumped the packet of sheets on her bed, then sat down beside them.

'Any other reason for this sudden departure?' she said. 'Apart from Sadie, I mean?'

'I'm going to college,' I said. 'I've decided.'

'What? *Study!*' said Judy in a voice so full of horror

that I had to laugh.

'Why not?'

'But you hated school – you couldn't wait to leave.'

'That was school. This is college. It's different. And frankly Sadie was a whole lot worse than school. Except that I did get paid to put up with her. But I'll get paid a whole lot more with some qualifications.'

'Oh, yeah? Haven't you heard about unemployment figures? There are people with *degrees* who can't get jobs!'

'I'm not going to get a degree,' I said. 'I'm going to do something that everyone wants, so I'll get a job. It's as simple as that.'

'Like what?' she said, still disbelieving.

'It's nice when your friends believe in you,' I said sarcastically. 'I don't know yet. But I'll think of something. Like computers, probably. Everyone wants people who know how to work computers.'

'I can work a computer,' said Judy, 'but I'm not going to college for a bit of paper to tell people I can.'

'All right, clever clogs,' I retorted. 'I bet there's more to it than what you can do. Not that I'm being rude or anything, but it's only sense, isn't it?'

'Okay, you win. I don't know anything really. Now that that's settled, what have we got to eat?'

'Eat?' I squeaked. 'I've only got something for me.'

'I know,' she said good humouredly, 'but what I meant was, what have you got for *you* to see if it will go with what I've got for *me* and if it does shall we share it?'

Later, I told her about Paul.

96

'So?' she said, after I'd explained – probably too much.

'So what?'

'So what are you worried about? As far as I can see, first, you might never see him again, and if you do it will be with Sam and me and there's no reason why you shouldn't see him while you're with us and be in a four, like we were with Mike.'

'That's really the problem,' I said. 'I don't want it to be like Mike. I'd be two-timing him. I wouldn't want him to do that to me, so I won't do it to him.'

'I can't see that just going around with a friend is two-timing. I bet Mike's in the same company as plenty of other girls.'

Jealousy raised its ugly head again. I didn't want to *think* of Mike with anybody else, let alone see him. And I knew it was stupid of me, because there was no reason at all why I should assume Mike was treating any of these girls as a girl-friend, or having some kind of relationship with them.

'It's because he hasn't written, isn't it?' said Judy shrewdly, watching the emotions that were obviously showing in my face. 'I knew there was something wrong when we had our row. I'm really ever so *ever so* sorry about that – I ought to have been a bit more understanding.'

'Don't be silly,' I said. 'I was horrible and I deserved it and anyway it wasn't because Mike hadn't written, it was because of Sadie and I should have done something about Sadie years ago.'

'But you see,' she went on as if I'd never interrupted, 'it won't do any harm at all to go out with someone else, just as friends, because I think and I've always thought that I don't see why you can't have men friends as well as women friends.'

'We do,' I said.

'No we don't. Not *friends*. Boy-friends, yes, but that's different. No, I meant real friends. Like you and me.'

'Nobody would believe you,' I said.

'That's the trouble,' agreed Judy.

But when Paul turned up later that evening to see if Judy had returned I knew that however much it would solve my guilt feelings, I couldn't think of him as a friend. It was lucky, I told myself, that he only dropped in for five minutes because he was going to be busy doing something else. I saw Judy's eyes on me, but she didn't comment, not even when he had gone. There was no mention of going out for a meal this time. I wondered bleakly whether I'd thrown too much cold water on what could have been a developing relationship.

When we'd finished washing up after our soup (the tin I'd agonized over) and were sitting companionably together, gossiping as hard as we ever did, I said suddenly, 'It's a bit silly going on about this loyalty thing, you know.'

'How's that?' said Judy lazily from her remade bed.

'Well, we've been assuming that Paul is at all interested and *wants* to see me, in any kind of way, girl-friendy or other-sort-of-friendy. What will really happen, of course, is that he'll never turn up again.'

'End of a beautiful friendship before it's even started, you mean?' said Judy. 'Yes, quite probably. In that case you haven't got anything to worry about, have you?'

Finally, Mike's letter came.

I went off to our private loo to read it.

He'd been getting on all right, he said. There were good lectures and bad lectures and he thought he was doing okay at the practical work because he'd done it all before and it was dead easy. Though of course you never knew whether you were doing it they way they wanted.

There was lots of this and more about the really great people he'd met (not to mention the really great pubs he'd been to). And finally, baldly, 'Love, Mike.'

Nothing about how was I, how was I settling down in my new life. Nothing about how Jude and I were getting on.

And nothing about how he loved me.

Somehow, even though you know a relationship is dying, and even though it looks as if there is the possibility of a new one which might take its place, it makes you very miserable. I sat and just let the tears roll down my cheeks, remembering all the nice times, remembering how his kisses excited me, how his arms made me shiver all over.

I had to make myself mop up the tears and wash my face in cold water before repairing my make-up. But it was worth it. Putting on a new face makes you able to cope with things better. I looked at myself in the mirror and said solemnly, 'It's time you went to see him.'

That was it. I'd go to Manchester and actually see him, see how I felt about him now that he'd been away for a few weeks. It might be that he was just rotten at writing letters. I didn't know. We'd never been apart before, since we started going out together a year ago.

And I'd put all thoughts of Paul resolutely out of my mind till then.

Chapter 8

It turned out it wasn't as easy as all that. All that stuff Judy had been saying about men friends, well, it may have been true, but I had to admit to myself that although Paul had behaved towards me in a way that was simply friendly, nothing else, I couldn't deny the way my body felt. And went on feeling. I was beginning to *dream* of him now.

And if I'd been bored and lonely when Judy was out in the evenings before, I was even more bored and lonely now, with no job to go to in the daytime.

I refused to go home to my parents, especially since they weren't very happy at the way I'd chucked up my job with nothing else to go to. And after I'd sorted things out with the Social Security and sent off for prospectuses for colleges and roughed out a letter asking if they had any unexpected vacancies, there was precious little left to do. I walked miles. I read the library dry. I even tried to sort out my knitting but eventually threw the lot into the dustbin, needles and all, because I was so fed up with it.

If only Mike would write and say I could go and visit, I might have been happier. I needed to sort my feelings out, not because of the way I was feeling about Paul whom I might never see again, but because I had this uneasy feeling that Mike didn't really care for me the way I thought I'd cared for him.

Jude and Sam asked if I'd like to go out with them, and I did a couple of times that week. But I felt uncomfortable with them, as if I had no right to be there at all. It was fine when were were sitting together in the warmth of the pub, or, on the other occasion, next to them in the cinema, but afterwards . . . Perhaps I was being too sensitive, perhaps they genuinely didn't mind me walking beside them while their arms tightened visibly round each other. But I minded.

'No, thanks,' I said on Saturday night when Judy pressed me to go out with them to a disco. 'I'd really rather stay here.'

'Are you all right, Sue?' asked Judy anxiously, because she knows any mention of a disco and normally I'm there like a shot. She also knows I don't mind if I don't have anyone in particular to go with — there's always someone you can dance with, and I can quite happily sit and lose myself in the music all night.

'I'm perfectly all right, I'd just rather stay here, that's all.'

'You're not saying no just because it's with Sam and me, are you?'

Of course it was, but I couldn't tell her that. I just mumbled something not very convincing, and wished for the hundredth time that I hadn't refused to go for a pizza with Paul.

'Are you sure you'll be all right?' asked Judy anxiously.

'Perfectly sure,' I said. 'Honestly, I think I need an early night.'

'On Saturday? You haven't got to get up for anything, not even to sign on!'

'I know, but I don't seem to be able to sleep properly just now,' I told her.

She gave me another worried look, and said, 'If you change your mind, you know where we are.'

'Thanks,' I said. 'I might do that, if I get bored.'

I knew I wouldn't go, even though the disco wasn't very far away and I knew a lot of other people who would be going. I'd felt so miserable this last week that I just couldn't face meeting people. If Mike had written – but he hadn't, so there was no point even in thinking about it.

I realized how empty my life was. I didn't seem to have anything. At least at home I could talk to Mum or Dad or even, if we were in the right mood, my sisters. It was company. And there was a television. I'd scorned watching it when I was at home, telling the gogglers that they were being mindless morons. (Me! Who was I to talk?) But I'd have welcomed any of those mindless, moronic programmes at this moment.

The door bell went.

'Will you answer it, Sue?' said Judy, on the last stages of her eye make-up. She was on her second go at it, as a bit of eye-shadow dust had gone under one of her contact lenses and she'd cursed and sworn and yelled and cried and had to wipe it all off and start again. 'It'll only be Sam.'

'Poor Sam,' I said, making for the door, 'to be called "only". I wouldn't stand for that, Sa . . . '

'Hello,' said Paul.

Why do people behave like complete pillocks when they're startled and surprised?

'I was just saying she shouldn't call Sam "only". It might give him an inferiority complex. Does it take you that way when you've been going out together that long?' I babbled. Not even 'Hello' in return.

'I wouldn't know,' said Paul as if my rambling was a completely rational question worthy of an answer. 'I don't think I've gone out with anyone long enough to find out whether I'd take them for granted. I don't think I'd ever take you for granted, though.'

'You're just saying that,' I grinned, to cover up the painful jump my heart had made.

'No, I'm not. Though I suppose after a thousand years you might have lost a tiny bit of your beauty.'

It was too extravagant to take seriously. 'I didn't know beauty had anything to do with taking people for granted. How about when I stop being unpredictable and start doing what you expect?' I riposted. 'Wouldn't you start taking me for granted then?'

'Oh, possibly,' said Paul. 'I might begin to think you were going to refuse to make my breakfast every day instead of on alternate Sundays. Or that you might even ask me in when I'm standing on a doorstep.'

'Oh, sorry!' I stammered, suddenly confused, backing away so that he could enter.

'Who are you talking to . . . ' began Judy, one eye

closed and the other obscured by her mascara brush. She took the brush away from her eye and looked lop-sidedly at us. 'Oh, it's Paul. Sam will be here soon.'

'I haven't come to see Sam,' said Paul in his direct way. 'I just wondered if Sue could give me a cup of coffee or something. I've brought the book I told you about.'

I'd forgotten. It was one of those things people say to you and you never really expect them to keep their word. The film we saw last week was a science fiction film, and he'd got a book by the same person who'd written the screenplay. I had been genuinely interested, and said I'd love to read the book.

'I'll put the kettle on,' I said. 'Take a seat.'

Paul sat down while Judy finished her other eye to match. 'Going somewhere nice?' he asked her conversationally.

'Disco. Why don't you come?'

I could have killed her. Yes, I know I said I wanted to be on my own. I know he was Sam's friend. I know I'd said I didn't want to go out with Paul even if he asked me because of my loyalty to Mike. I know I hadn't really agreed with Judy when she talked about friendship between men and women.

But I wanted him to myself. I wanted – perhaps to try out having a platonic friendship. I wanted *company*. I wanted to sit and talk about science fiction and films and music, I didn't want him to go out and leave me.

'I don't know,' said Paul slowly. 'I hadn't – how do you feel, Sue? Would you like to come out to a disco?'

'I *was* going to have a quiet evening at home,' I said.

'I've been trying to persuade her all day,' said Judy, not entirely accurately, and I forgave her for what I thought she'd meant.

'Do you want to be persuaded?' asked Paul with a twinkle in his eye.

'I'd have to get changed,' I hesitated.

'That's a big hint for you to go away for ten minutes,' said Judy in her direct way. 'We haven't got another room, except the kitchen which isn't big enough to hold the cooker let alone another person, or the loo, which is a bit freezing.'

'Supposing I go and sit in the loo for ten minutes,' joked Paul, 'if Sue really wants to go.' He looked at me enquiringly. 'You said you wanted an evening to yourself. Don't let anyone bully you.'

I smiled. 'I don't really mind being bullied,' I said. 'I just didn't want to play gooseberry to those two any more.'

'Sue! You said it wasn't because of that!' scolded Judy. 'We don't mind – honestly.'

'I mind,' I said. 'And I can't expect you *not* to hold hands just because I'm there.'

This time, in the middle of Judy's huffing and protesting, the ring at the door really was Sam, and the problem of me getting changed was solved by Paul suggesting he and Sam went round the corner for half a pint before coming back to pick us both up.

'There you are,' said Judy proudly, as if she'd accomplished something.

'What do you mean "There you are"?' I grumbled. 'I told you what I felt about two-timing Mike.'

'And I told you you weren't two-timing him,' said Judy patiently. 'Now get changed quickly for God's sake, because I don't want to shove them *both* in the loo when they get back.'

I decided that I'd treat it as just that, and really enjoyed myself at the disco. Paul liked dancing, and was quite willing to be on the floor all the time.

But he wasn't a silent dancer, and in spite of the noise hammering our eardrums from the disco, we talked and talked as we moved our bodies to the beat. Or rather, looking back, it was Paul who asked questions, and me who answered, so that he managed to find out all kinds of things about me without me really noticing I'd told him.

We sat down at last and the moment I'd dreaded – and hoped for – happened. He took my hand, and pins and needles shot up my arm. I closed my eyes.

'Sue . . .'

Please don't ask me anything I can't answer, I prayed.

'Sue, I . . .'

But he for once was just as lost for words as I was. His hand crept up my arm to my shoulder and ended up pulling my head gently round towards him.

The kiss was magical. I melted into him, not noticing the discomfort of the chair, the edges of the table.

I won't tell you the silly things we said. They're so wonderful at the time, but if you think about them later it sounds as if you've gone bananas. In any case, that part is all private.

We didn't dance any more, but Judy and Sam did – just to leave us alone, I think. I blessed her for her tact. I forgot all about Mike, until Paul brought the subject up some time later.

'I've got to know,' he said directly.

'What about?' I hedged, feeling panic spread through me.

'Do you really miss him?'

'I thought I did,' I said, 'but he's only written to me once since he went away, and he didn't say much then.'

'I didn't say did *he* miss *you*,' Paul said significantly.

'Not now,' I said, and thought I was being honest. Even so, I think I was afraid of being more closely questioned, so I countered it with one of my own. 'It's time you stopped talking about me. You know all about my private life, and my lack of job and things. I never asked what do you do?'

'For a living? Not a lot. Well, that's not true. I have a boring job in a building society. Though I hope when I get further on it won't be so boring and I might, just might, get on well enough to earn quite a bit in management.'

'Good for you,' I said. 'That's what I should have done, instead of wasting my small talents in that shop. Did I tell you I'd given in my notice?'

'Really? Tell me.'

'I'm supposing to be talking about you,' I reminded him. 'It's not very interesting, really. I just got fed up with the whole thing. I'm going to go to college, I think.'

'Brilliant idea,' said Paul. 'I tell you what – I'm going to this evening class, making my own guitar. Why don't you come along too?'

The insecure feeling I still had underneath, that this was just a one-night thing, was dispelled in an instant.

'*Making* a *guitar*?'

'It's possible. Hard, but possible,' he said. 'I'd always wanted to do something with my hands, and the chap who teaches is really good.'

'Don't be daft, Paul, I couldn't make a guitar!' I said.

'Why not? I don't see why you shouldn't.'

'But I'm a girl . . . ' and I stopped. No. This was what Judy and I had been talking about. We were as good as men any day. If Paul could make a guitar, I didn't see why I couldn't.

'What day? Not that it matters. I'm not doing anything . . . '

'Wednesdays,' he said immediately. 'And people are at all different stages, so you wouldn't feel as if you were holding things up, not like typewriting courses or anything like that. Honestly, I'd love you to come with me. They've got all the tools which you can borrow: you don't even have to fork out much money,' as if this could be the only reason I might not want to go.

'I could give it a try, I suppose,' I said guardedly.

'And if you didn't like it, nobody's making you go on with it,' he said reasonably.

'You know,' I said, 'that's one of the really nice things about leaving school. Even if you end up absolutely skint or miserable or even deliriously happy, you don't *have* to do it.'

'Too true.' He laughed. 'When I sit at that counter, trying to find out why I'm five hundred quid short today and wondering why I've let myself in for this damned silly job and knowing it's mostly for the money, I'll remember what you've said.'

'And I'll remember you've said "Why not?" if ever I say I can't do something,' I said.

'Right. Let's both decide to make life as interesting as it can be, and to hell with convention!'

'Taking of convention,' I said, 'discos are conventionally places to dance and it'll be ending soon and this record happens to be my favourite . . . '

I was exhilarated and happy and not in the least bit tired when we got back to the flat.

He didn't stay. He waited until I'd found my key and let myself into the room.

'Thanks for coming out with me,' he said. And his arms folded round me as if I was the most natural place for them to be. 'I want to stay with you, I want to be with you always, but not now. You've got to make sure how you feel about Mike.' My heart thumped hard then. Was I deceiving Paul? More to the point, was I deceiving Mike? I didn't want to think about it. I wanted to be carried off by Paul and not have to decide anything for myself ever again. I'd never felt so wonderful nor so unhappy mixed together in my whole life. I scarcely heard him say when he'd meet me on Wednesday, but watched him walk down the path, away from me, out of my life even for a few days.

'Paul!' I wanted to tell him I was quite sure, that I would write to Mike instantly and tell him it was all off. I wanted him to turn and come back to me. But my voice was hoarse, too thin to carry in the night air. And then there was Judy and Sam, saying goodnights as they passed him. It was too late.

But only for tonight. Before Wednesday, I'd write to

Mike, then I could tell Paul how I felt with a clear conscience.

The only trouble was, Mike's letter, saying he'd be really pleased if I could come to Manchester to see him next Wednesday, arrived the next morning.

Chapter 9

I had to go. I had to make quite sure. Even though this letter was as terse and unromantic as his first had been. He just wasn't much of a letter writer. I couldn't judge him on that. (I tried not to feel that he not only didn't like putting down that sort of stuff on paper, he wasn't even very good at it for real, in the dark!) But I thought I had to tell him properly. It was only fair. We'd been going out for so long.

The silly conversation I'd had with Paul on the door step before we went out last night – last *night*! it seemed like a hundred years ago – came back into my mind. About being taken for granted. I knew Mike took me for granted. It didn't occur to him that I might need to be cherished. Perhaps that was an old-fashioned word, but it was what I felt I needed right at this moment. And it didn't at all clash with my ideas about wanting to be independent and my own person. It wasn't the same as being *owned*.

To be honest, I was really quite scared of going up to

Manchester. I didn't know how I was going to react to Mike. Would I suddenly realize I adored him after all? Or, worse, would I *know* I'd been right about my feelings for Paul? If so, I didn't know quite what I was going to say to him. He wasn't the type to hit me, as I'd already explained to Judy, but I wasn't quite sure what he *would* do! And I felt really worried that he hadn't said a dicky bird about anything I'd said in my letters — particularly the last one where I'd told him about my row with Sadie and giving up my job. I'd have thought he'd have tons to say about that. Unless of course he was saving up his scorn for when I saw him.

Or even feeling glad about it because he'd think, of course, that I'd go straight home to Mum where he thought I ought to be.

But there were other things to think about. I had an interview at the pub at eleven o'clock. I hoped against hope that I would get the job, not just because I needed the money but because I needed to be able to consolidate the self-respect I'd found by giving in my notice to Sadie. I wanted it to have been a sensible decision, not the action of a bloody fool.

But all the time I got myself ready I was wondering about Mike. Wondering whether his passionless letters were really because he wasn't very good at them, or whether they were because he didn't care about me.

He'd asked me to Manchester, hadn't he? He couldn't hate me that much. And he'd even suggested a day. Which meant he might be organizing things — perhaps booking a table in a restaurant if he had enough money for such an extravagance, or if not, perhaps finding a good film to see in the afternoon. At the very least, showing me off to his new friends. He would have to be organized when his girl-friend was coming up only for a day.

I was working on what I would have done if it had been me.

I wondered if he'd have minded if I'd suddenly turned up, like I thought he had the night Paul first arrived with Sam . . .

And that was another thing: all thought of Paul had to be completely erased from my mind.

And the best way of doing that, I thought, was to go out and get that job before I wrote to say what train I was getting on Wednesday, in case I was supposed to be working then. You can hardly be given a job and then say immediately you can't work the days they ask you because you want to go out!

I wondered what Judy would say when I told her.

'One day,' she said, crashing in at the door, and throwing her handbag right across the room, 'I shall be on time for work.'

'Weren't you?' I asked cheekily.

'You know ruddy well I wasn't. Yeah, okay, it's my own fault. I shall have to do something about it. But I got a tiny telling off today.'

I couldn't help smiling. 'Have a cuppa,' I said soothingly. 'At least you have a job.'

'I won't have one if I go on like this,' she said gloomily, 'and for a lot less good reason than the reason you haven't got one. Oh, well. I ought to have gone in for something which started a bit later – like being a barmaid. Heck, that reminds me! How did you get on with your interview?

'I got the job,' I said with a smirk. 'Who says there aren't any jobs?'

'Great! When do you start?' said Judy immediately.

I looked at my watch. 'In about half an hour,' I said.

'Good God!'

'Only part time, but it all helps.'

'Is it worth it?' asked Judy, 'I mean, it can't be much more than the dole, can it?'

'Just about less, I think,' I told her, 'but they're taking on permanent staff next month, and said if that's what I wanted, and they were satisfied with me, then I'd get it.'

'Even better!' said Judy. 'I suppose that means you'll never be able to get me up in the morning?'

'I doubt whether I'll be able to get myself to stay awake all evening!' I said ruefully. 'You know what I'm like after ten.'

'Tell you what, swap jobs,' she said.

'It wouldn't be a bad idea at that,' I told her.

It wasn't until I was nearly out of the door that I remembered about Mike.

'Oh, by the way,' I said, 'I got a letter from Mike this morning.'

'Fantastic!' said Judy. Then, 'Everything okay?' she said belatedly.

'He wants me to go up and see him on Wednesday.'

'Can you?' she asked. 'I mean, will you be working?'

'By great good luck, they don't need anyone extra on Wednesdays,' I said, 'so I won't have to tell him.'

'Hang on, though,' as I was halfway through the door. 'Didn't you write and tell him . . . ?'

'Must have crossed in the post,' I said, and escaped before she could ask more of the kind of questions I didn't want to answer.

I wanted to go straight away. But the first day off I'd have was tomorrow, and there simply wouldn't be enough time. Especially if the post was a bit funny to his college. After that they wanted me to come in every day until the next Wednesday, because they were a bit short-staffed. Though this wouldn't happen every week, it did mean a bit more money this week so I'd be able to buy something new to wear, to meet Mike. I know I ought to have saved it up for the rent, and to pay for the heating, but it seemed a special occasion. I'd found out about the train fares, and I could get a cheap day return, giving me even more of an excuse to buy something new with what I'd thought of now as the change from the proper fare.

It was going to be really great, I thought, working in this pub. I did hope I'd get on with the people all right, they seemed very nice at first glance. I hoped I'd manage the work as well – still, at least I knew how to work a till! And another good thing about it was that sometimes I had whole days off, and only went in at eight o'clock in the evening. Even my first day, tomorrow, didn't start until quarter to eleven, halfway through the morning.

But what should I buy to wear to Manchester? I walked round all the shops, not really enjoying looking at the clothes because it seemed to matter so much that I bought the right thing.

There was this wonderful velvet evening skirt, for instance, and a blouse that went with it that was shimmery and loose and had a sparkling silver thread in the weave. But this was a normal sort of desperately wanting – the sort of thing that Judy and I, when we were still at school and spent our Saturday mornings in town going round the shops, would have gone back to time and again just to drool over. In a silly sort of way it was really nice to drool, even though there wasn't a Judy there to do it with me.

But I had to be sensible. I was buying something to wear on a train, and to have on all day and still look nice.

I saw it. The perfect dress. It was fun and bright purple and slightly way-out and I absolutely loved it. I went into the changing room, and it fitted me as if it had been specially made for me. It had padded shoulders, a tight-fitting waist and a wide, long skirt. I looked great in it and the price was just right. I could even afford to put a bit of heating money away if I got this.

The only thing was, I knew Mike would absolutely hate it.

'Any good?' said the bored girl at the entrance to the changing cubicles as I walked out with my three dresses on their hangers.

'Sorry. Doesn't fit,' I lied, and handed them over, walking quickly out of the shop before I changed my mind and bought it regardless.

And the really stupid thing was that if I'd been absolutely sure I loved Mike I'd have got it anyway, and if I'd been absolutely sure I didn't I'd have got it anyway. It was not really knowing that made me feel it wouldn't be fair on Mike to wear something I knew he'd loathe and be rude about.

I'd practically searched the entire town before I made up my mind. The skirt was really nice. I did like it, it wasn't just that I knew Mike would like me in it. And then with a kind of despairing madness I picked up the matching jacket and took that over to the counter too.

It was far more than I could afford. I should never have bought it. I did feel good in the whole two-piece, and I knew Mike would like me in it, but as soon as I got home I felt guilty. I'd spent all the money I hadn't yet earned this week, and left nothing over for rent or anything.

I went and got my train ticket after that, just to make sure I hadn't bought the damned thing for nothing.

It was the right thing to have bought. I knew it. I felt absolutely right in the carriage watching the names of the stations as they went by, counting the minutes until we got there.

'Mike!' He looked just the same — or perhaps slightly scruffier. He obviously hadn't gone to much trouble to dress up for me, I thought, then with annoyance dismissed the thought from my head. I couldn't go criticizing him just for that, I told myself fiercely. Men never did dress up, I ought to be used to it.

His tousled head turned on the platform. He said something to someone next to him, then walked lazily down the platform to where I was waving excitedly from the half-open door.

'Watch it. You might hurt yourself.'

'Mike! It's wonderful to see you!'

He gave me a perfunctory kiss. 'Had a good journey?'

'Fine, yes. I nearly got off at the station before last, but then I realized . . .'

Then I realized he wasn't listening. His eyes were fixed somewhere straight ahead. But then it was very crowded: he was trying to get out of the place as quickly as possible.

We stood outside, at a very draughty bus stop, for what seemed like hours.

'I should have worn something warmer,' I joked, shivering. Now was the cue for him to say something nice about my two-piece.

'It is a bit chillier here, isn't it?' he said amicably. 'Rains a lot, too.'

'Where are we going?' I asked, tucking my arm in his and cuddling into his coat.

'Thought you'd like a look around the place,' he said. 'Meet a few of my mates.'

'Great,' I said, trying to be enthusiastic. Probably when I got out of this biting wind I'd feel a bit more comfortable. Though in fact it didn't feel very much warmer on the bus. Mike ran upstairs to the top deck and I struggled after him in my tight skirt and high heels.

'Wait a minute!' I protested. 'I'm stuck.'

He laughed, and pulled at my arm as I reached the top. 'Should wear more sensible clothes,' he said.

That was all – absolutely all – he ever said about my two-piece the whole day.

Still, you couldn't expect him to notice, not really. He was busy showing me all over his college – it was awfully big, because I wouldn't have remembered whether this one was the common room, that one the coffee bar, or the next one a lecture room. And then there were his friends. They all seemed very nice, if a little remote. Then we'd been having a quick cup of coffee and Mike had seen several people he knew. It was all the, 'Hi, Mike', 'Hi, Rick', 'This is Sue,' 'Hi, Sue,' sort of thing, then they went off with their own friends and Mike seemed to hang about restlessly, as if wondering what to do with me. The last one was just the same, only he didn't go away.

'Hi, Tony.'

'Hi, Mike?' looking hard at me.

'This is Sue. My girl-friend from home.'

'Pleased to meet you, Sue. Listen, have you done that work for tomorrow? I couldn't borrow your notes could I? I had a sort of hangover on Monday and never got to the lecture.'

'Sure, man. When do you want them?'

'Well, like – now.'

'Have to come back to my digs, then. Sorry, Sue, but you were a bit bored by the place, weren't you? I could see it in your face.'

'No, I wasn't,' I said. 'It's just that you were going a bit quickly and I didn't have much chance . . . '

' . . . won't take a minute. You don't mind walking about half a mile, do you, Sue? We don't get the buses much. They cost quite a bit, and out of a grant . . . '

'When you'd rather spend the money on beer,' agreed Tony.

I half ran, half walked beside their long strides, and my feet felt colder and colder. And I felt really miserable for some reason — it was a kind of feeling I didn't recognize because I hadn't really ever had it before. And as Mike and Tony were talking about electronics, interspersed with pronouncements on beer and reminiscences of parties they had been to during the last few weeks, I had plenty of time to try and identify the feeling. I tried to relate it to the other time I do remember feeling the same way, but it was an elusive memory, and each time I tried to catch it it seemed to go away. It had something to do with a holiday, I do know that, and I couldn't think why I should be so miserable on holiday.

The memory of sun and the smell of sea rushed back, and almost warmed my numbed fingers. There was a little girl I had played with, but I couldn't see my sisters . . .

It came back suddenly, in a rush. Jenny and Chris both had had measles, and rather than make me miss my holiday (or more probably get me out of the way so that I didn't cause problems by being rudely healthy when my sisters were miserably ill), an aunt whom at the time I didn't know very well had offered to take me with them to the seaside. I must have been about thirteen. Quite old enough not to be homesick, but for some reason I was.

And now I had recognized it.

I wanted to go home.

'All right, Sue?'

'A bit cold,' I said. 'You're right, I should have worn something warmer.'

'I'll make a special effort and put my gas fire on for you,' he said.

'Wow!' I said, half mocking, half really appreciating it. 'And can I stay there for the rest of the day?'

'Unless you want to come out for something to eat, of course.'

It was nearly lunch time, and I suddenly felt extremely hungry.

'Where are we going? Anywhere special?'

'Where shall we go, Tony?' asked Mike.

And then real misery enveloped me. He hadn't thought about where he was going to take me. We weren't going anywhere special. He really didn't care about me. I might just as well have stayed at home.

'You won't want me hanging about,' said Tony. 'I'll just grab your notes and run. I need to copy them up and then do some work on it.'

I could have kissed Tony, even if I hadn't ever met him before.

And then we were at Mike's digs.

It was a room. Just a room, with a bed in it. Rather a feminine pink-counterpaned bed, with a wardrobe and a chest of drawers. It wasn't very tidy. But then, nor was ours.

'Where ever do you cook?' I asked him while he was sorting through a pile of ring-binders on top of the dressing table.

'Cook?' he said absently. 'Hang on. I think this is the one, isn't it?'

He handed a blue binder to Tony.

'That's the one, man. I'm really grateful, you know that. Do the same for you.'

'Ha ha,' said Mike. 'That'll be the day. I want it back by Saturday, though.'

'Oh, get it before then,' said Tony. 'Tomorrow, with luck. Must go. See you.'

'Can I put on the fire?' I said.

'Sure. Help yourself.'

And as Mike showed Tony out I went down on my knees and had a look to see how it worked. There was a box of matches nearby, and a few spent ones littered on the hearth, so I switched on and lit it, sitting on the floor close to the welcome flames and warming my hands.

'Want some lunch, then?' he said.

'Give us a minute, Mike,' I shivered. 'I'm freezing.'

'Be warm down the pub.'

'All right,' I sighed, and got up, turning the fire off as I did so.

'That's a good girl,' Mike approved. 'Save the pennies, eh?'

I wasn't going to get irritated. I refused to get irritated. I'd come to see Mike, who was still, until either of us said anything, my boy-friend. Perhaps when we got to the pub and could sit down in the warm and have something to eat he'd be nice to me, make me feel his special girl who had come all this way just to see him.

I did feel better with half a pint in front of me and good smells of cooking. There was a roaring fire in the corner, and we were early enough to get seats next to it. As I thawed, so did Mike seem to.

'Well, tell me what you've been up to,' he said.

'I bet you don't read my letters,' I complained.

'I do. I just want to hear it all from you.' And he hugged me. 'What do you want to drink? The menu's

121

on the bar, but the thing they do best is either chilli con carne or ploughman's.'

Oh – a chilli, please,' I said meekly, not asking to see the rest. I did know, after all, what it cost to live on one's own, and I didn't want to ask for chicken or scampi or something he wouldn't be able to afford, though the smell of them cooking made my mouth water. 'How are you getting on on your own, Mike? Where do you cook? Do you share a kitchen or some thing? I didn't see a gas ring or anything.'

'Me, cook? Do you think I'm off my head?'

I didn't quite understand. 'You mean you don't have breakfast? Oh, Mike, do you think that's good for you? I keep having arguments with Judy about this . . .'

'I have breakfast all right,' he said, 'if I get up in time for it, but the landlady's pretty good and I can leave it up to half past nine. You've made up your mind, then? Chilli, is it? Two chillis and two pints.'

'Half,' I corrected, wishing pubs did coffees because I could do with something warm in my stomach. Still, maybe the chilli would do that. But don't pubs do coffee as well if they do meals? 'Mike? Could I have a coffee instead of a drink? I'm really cold.'

'Oh, no,' he groaned, 'you haven't gone even more teetotal since I've been away, have you? Listen, they know me here. I don't want them to be ashamed of me!'

But he went to the bar fairly good humouredly. I had time to think, while he was waiting, that only a couple of months ago I wouldn't have had the nerve to ask Mike to change the order from alcohol to coffee in case he laughed at me. Perhaps living on my own had given me a very small bit of independence.

I had to think this, I had to make myself feel satisfied with myself, or I'd have burst into tears. This wasn't what I'd expected when Mike had invited me to spend the day with him. He hadn't done anything special for me. It was as if I'd seen him every day for the last weeks since he went to college. I was being as taken for granted as I was when he was with me at home.

'There we are,' he said, plonking down his pint and a slopped over cup of coffee.

'Thanks. It's nice not to have to cook my own for a change.'

'Your Mother making you do a lot, is she?'

'Mum?' I said, puzzled at first, then annoyed that he'd thought exactly what I thought he'd think. 'But I'm not with Mum, Mike, you know that. Listen, I must tell you what we've done with the flat: you know that chair we kept on falling over, where you had to sit, well we had the most incredible idea and put it . . . '

As I chattered happily telling him about the flat and what we'd done to it his eyes roamed the room, as if looking for someone. But perhaps he was only waiting for the meal to turn up. I was feeling pretty hungry myself.

'Ah, there it is,' said Mike, getting up and taking the tray from the girl with more manners, I thought resentfully, than he would ever have had for me. 'Thanks, Carol.'

'See you tomorrow, I suppose,' she said, and waved the emptied tray at him.

'You don't always eat here, do you?' I said. 'They

seem to know you pretty well.'

'It's nearby,' said Mike. 'Easy, and quite cheap.'

It didn't seem to occur to him that he was insulting me by telling me everything was cheap. The lump in my throat made it difficult to swallow the chilli con carne, which was not bad but had more beans than meat in and the sauce wasn't as fiery as I'd have liked. But I was quibbling. He was *paying* for me, wasn't he. He'd *asked* me to come.

'It would be a lot cheaper if you cooked for yourself,' I said, really just to make conversation, but Mike seemed to take it the wrong way.

'I don't see why I should,' he said. 'I've got too many other things to do to have time to cook. I don't need to.'

I caught on at last. 'You have bed and breakfast?' I said, realizing.

'What did you expect me to do?' said Mike.

'I just thought – oh, never mind, it doesn't matter.'

'How's work, then?' he said. 'Old Sadie still a pain?'

'Mike! I told you I'd finished there!'

'Oh, so you did. That's right. Well, I don't suppose it matters much. And you've gone back home.'

'Mike,' I said dangerously, 'I just said I wasn't at home. I'm still at the flat. And I've got another job. In a pub.'

'Great. Good place for me to come and see you,' he said. 'Not that I think girls ought to work in pubs – it's a bit late, isn't it? You watch out when you come home.'

'It's only round the corner, at the Mitre,' I said meekly.

'Oh, well, should be all right.'

'And what about your work?' I said, eager to be interested in what *he* was doing.

Mike told me, not very enthusiastically, about what he was doing, then went up for another pint while I toyed with the remains of my chilli. I tried hard not to compare him with Paul. I *mustn't* compare him with Paul. They were different people, and I'd got to make up my mind, each on their own merits.

'What shall we do for the rest of the time before I go for my train?' I said. 'Is there anywhere nice to go?'

'Pity you can't stay,' said Mike, and my heart leaped. 'Still the landlady would notice. See, you don't have to worry about me – I don't have any choice about being good.'

'I wasn't worried,' I said. 'Not about that, anyway.'

'What's that supposed to mean?' said Mike.

'Oh, nothing,' I said, because I wasn't really sure what I *did* mean. Except that being jealous of girls wasn't the only thing one could get worried about. And I wondered how much he wanted me to stay, and how much he just wanted me in his bed for the night. 'I wouldn't have been able to stay, anyway. I've got to work tomorrow lunch time.'

'Where shall we go now, then? Back to my room?'

I had a nasty feeling that, landlady or not, Mike wasn't to be trusted on his own in that room with the pink bedspread. As Judy said, why do they make them look so much like *bedrooms*?

'I'm not in a hurry to leave here,' I said, and truthfully had only just begun to feel comfortable as the chill left my body. The fire was more attractive than Mike's gas fire, anyway.

'Another drink, then?'

He didn't seem too bothered to go and do anything else. Perhaps he felt, too, that if I didn't want to go and do whatever he wanted in his bare little room, then we might just as well stay in the only sort of place where he really felt at home.

'If they've got some more coffee . . . '

And there we stayed, until closing time, when I said it was time for me to get on a train and return home. Mike didn't argue, though he must have known as well as I did that there were plenty of trains, going on until fairly late in the evening.

He put his arm round me as we waited for the bus to take us back to the station, and I felt some of the old excitement and love for him. But he'd changed so much. I didn't know whether I really wanted . . . but there would be time to think about that later.

'Love you,' he mumbled against my ear.

I couldn't say I loved him in return. I knew I didn't love him any more. But he didn't notice my silence.

He kissed me long and searchingly, and then the bus came.

'You wouldn't like to . . .' began Mike, his foot half on, half off.

'You can't . . . your landlady . . ' I said.

'Make up your minds,' said the driver grumpily and crashed into gear noisily.

We got on. Mike paid the fares. We sat down. I knew it was the end, and I thought Mike did too.

Until the train. He found me a seat, then I went to the

window to say goodbye. His hand covered mine and warmed it.

'You won't be in that place long,' he said.

'What place?' I said.

'That flat of yours. I knew you shouldn't have gone there. It was obvious from your letters you're not happy there.'

'Mike! That's an absolute lie!' I tried to think what I'd said, how I could have given him that impression.

'And of course you won't be able to afford it now. Not on part time. I could have told your parents at the time.'

It was as if he hadn't listened to a word I'd said, never read a single line of all those screeds I'd sent him.

'But you'll have to give in your notice, I suppose. Never mind. It's been an experience hasn't it? Showed you I was right after all?'

I didn't know what to say. My tongue seemed to have frozen. I just couldn't believe it. Through a rising tide of panic I heard the whistle blow, felt the shifting of wheels under the metal below my feet.

'I'm staying there,' I said, as the train edged its way out of the platform and Mike walked along with it.

'I'll be back in a fortnight. Half term,' he said. 'I'll see you at your parents'.'

The kiss was brief, and left me completely cold.

'No, Mike,' I said. 'I won't see you again. I'm sorry.'

It was cowardly, to do it that way, when he couldn't even answer as the train picked up speed. I watched him as he grew smaller on the platform. He lifted his hand in farewell, and was gone, forever.

Chapter 10

'Well?' said Judy.

'Well, what?' I said listlessly.

'Had a good day?'

'No.'

'Ah. Sorry about that.' Her eyebrows shot up to her fringe. 'Want to talk?'

'Not really. Not at the moment.'

'Cup of tea?'

I smiled faintly. Jude, offering me a cup of tea. I must look pretty grotty for her to do that.

'What did he think of the outfit, then? It's fabulous, isn't it? How much, or shouldn't I ask?'

I sat on the chair draped with one of Judy's best tapestries. I'd have been better sitting on the dull chintz underneath. I felt very much the same as I had that grey day when my parents had told me to move out.

'Obviously better not to ask,' said Judy. 'I suppose it was all a total disaster.'

'I feel such a bloody fool,' I said bitterly. 'Chasing after him when he obviously couldn't care less about me. I don't think he ever did, you know, Jude. I was just a convenient person who did as I was told and didn't argue much. That's why he got such a shock when I did argue and told him what I wanted! Remind me to avoid men for a while, will you?'

'No problem,' said Judy airily. 'Sam won't be around for some days, I shouldn't think, so we can have a nice female moan about men and a good old mutual admiration society for us.'

'You what?' I said, suddenly cottoning on. 'You haven't bust up, have you? Oh, Judy!'

'Not permanently,' she said calmly – a lot more calmly than I would have done, but then at that precise moment in time I was a seething mixture of disappointment, disillusionment, and plain annoyance. 'At least I don't think permanently, though I may change my mind. I was absolutely,' she went on, slightly muffled by the kitchen door behind which she was filling the kettle, 'fed up with him taking me for granted. You know we were supposed to be going to this party?'

'What party?' I still wasn't really interested in any one else's problems.

'*You* know,' she said impatiently, 'next Saturday, the one you aren't going to go to because you're working at the pub – Sandy Morrison's party.'

'Oh, that one. Go on.'

'Well, it's not important really, but I was quite looking forward to it because as you know I like parties.

'I know!' I said.

'Yeah, well, as I was saying, then Sam comes round just as I'd got back from work and says, "Sorry about Sandy's party but we won't be able to go." "We?" I said, "what do you mean, we? What you mean is, *you* can't go.' And he said he had to go with this aunt or whoever it was to take her to tea with his grandma and stay with them all evening so that they didn't quarrel, and since he couldn't go he didn't think I'd want to go without him. So I blew my top and said who did he think he was, my keeper, that I couldn't go anywhere without him? and he got in a huff because he said I shouldn't *want* to go anywhere without him, and . . . '

The kettle lid rattled and spluttered and the water boiled over and put out the gas while I laughed and laughed and began to feel as if I might be sane after all.

'Well . . . ' she said defensively, 'don't you think I was right? Stop laughing at me.'

'I'm not laughing at you,' I hiccupped. 'It's hysteria, I think. Oh, God, Jude, you've no idea what a terrible day I've had!'

'Just be thankful it's all over with,' said Judy. 'Now you can go out with Paul without feeling guilty.'

'I don't know that I want to,' I said slowly. 'For the moment I just want to crawl into a corner and lick my wounds.'

'You're just saying that,' said Judy cheerfully. 'I bet when he rings the bell you'll jump up and rush off without a backward glance.'

'Wanna bet?' I said. 'I told you, I've had it up to here with men.'

But when the bell went later on that evening I felt a shiver of excitement in spite of myself. I began to move towards the door, then checked myself, pretending I was sure it must be Sam. Judy looked at me wickedly and said, 'Go on. I dare you!'

'I'll put spiders in your soup!' I hissed at her, and clumped across the room to open the door.

Paul stood there, that wonderful warm smile on his face.

'Are you ready?' he asked.

'Ready?' I said blankly.

'For the guitar-making class.'

Oh, no! After all that had happened today I'd completely forgotten about it!

Judy snorted with laughter behind me. 'Don't you mean guitar *playing*?' she said.

'You keep out of this,' I ordered her. 'I'm going to *make* a guitar, and when I have I'll learn how to play it. Just wait and see. Yeah, I'm ready.'

'You look really great,' he said. 'New clothes? Or do you always look as if you've just stepped out of a magazine?'

I could have kissed him, right there and then in front of Judy! 'You say all the right things,' I told him gratefully. Best if I let him think I'd put them on specially for him, just because I'd newly bought them. 'But I've just thought,' which I truthfully just had, 'are they the right sort of clothes for carving bits of wood?'

'You might be more comfortable in jeans,' he said tactfully. 'Shall I go round the corner for half a pint or sit in the loo?'

'I'll hide behind the wardrobe door,' I said. 'Talk to Jude and look the other way for two seconds.'

I opened the wardrobe door and pulled on the jeans under my skirt. A nice picture of Paul would go better there than Elvis, I mused, feeling for the first time a dissatisfaction with my childhood idol. I stepped out of the skirt, threw it and the jacket onto a hanger, pulled a sweater over my head and shut the wardrobe door again.

'You meant it,' he said with astonishment.

'Of course I meant it,' I said. 'You haven't got another of these masculine pre-conceived ideas about women, have you?'

'Sorry,' he said. 'I can only go by my sister – she's the only woman I've known for long periods of time. She's the world's slowest. And changes her mind about fifty times as well.'

I almost felt sorry for Judy as we went out. Then I thought, no. I'd been left to myself for evenings on end while she was out with Sam. Not that I felt meanly triumphant or anything. Just not guilty.

I don't really remember much about that first evening, carving wood. It was very difficult, because I'd never done anything like it before, but Paul kept leaving his own instrument (which was beginning to look impressively like one) to come over and help me. Every time his hands brushed mine I felt an electric shock go through me, and I daren't meet his dark blue eyes in case everyone else noticed.

'Do you mind if I ask . . . ?' he said into my ear much later when we were outside the flat door, locked in each other's arms.

'Ask what?' I mumbled, drunk with happiness.

'About Mike.'

'What about Mike?' He didn't exist, not any more.

'Have you made up your mind?'

'It's all over,' I said.

'You've written to him?' he pressed.

'Yes,' I said. I couldn't be bothered to explain. And it didn't matter. It was the same thing. Better, even. I pulled down his head to my level and kissed his mouth, loving the startling softness of it after the hard roughness of his cheeks. His arms enfolded me and I felt at one with him, and the moon, and the stars, in the night.

*

I was working at eight on Thursday, so we hadn't arranged to meet. When the door bell rang at half past six I left Judy to open the door, thinking it must be Sam, coming to make up.

'It's Paul,' said my flat-mate.

I turned with a pleased jump of my heart and a welcoming smile on my face. Until I saw his face.

'Can I have a word with you, Sue?' he said distantly.

My heart began to beat loudly in my ears. I'd lost confidence after my day with Mike, and I suddenly didn't know how to cope with any kind of awkward situation. And what the hell was the matter anyway?'

'Sure,' I said stiffly. 'Do you want me to come out somewhere or shall I ask Jude to go?' I put that bit in with a certain amount of sarcasm, because I didn't think Paul was the type to be that selfish. It did throw him a bit, because the cold look on his face melted into slight confusion before straightening out again. 'We'll go to the pub,' he said.

'You mean would I mind coming out to the pub?' I said, feeling angrily that if all men were going to tell me what to do they could take a running jump.

'*Sorry*,' he said, without sounding sorry at all. 'Would madam *mind* walking out to the nearest hostelry with me in order to discuss a private matter?'

'She would, as a matter of fact,' I began, but Judy interrupted.

'I'm just going out, in fact, if you want to talk here.'

We stood in the doorway, glaring at each other, and I began to wonder what I'd ever seen in Paul. I hadn't *done* anything, for God's sake, so I couldn't see why he was behaving like this. I heard Jude collecting her things hastily behind me, and said 'Goodbye,' automatically as she brushed past on her way out. 'Back in an hour,' she hissed into my ear. An hour! I could be murdered in an hour.

But I was getting hysterical again. Coldly I motioned Paul to a seat and said, 'What's the matter?'

'You didn't tell me you were going to meet your boyfriend,' he said directly.

I felt anger rise like a tide.

'Do I have to tell you every small thing I do?' I said.

'Sam said . . . ' he began.

'Sam?' I said. 'What the hell has Sam got to do with it?'

'Apparently Judy told him, and he told me . . . '

'You bloody men are worse gossips than women are supposed to be,' I shouted furiously.

'So you didn't intend to tell me,' he said icily.

'Tell you what? There was nothing to tell. You don't own me, you know. I've had enough of that with Mike. And I can't really see what you're all upset about.'

'You said you'd written,' he said. It wasn't an accusation. It was a statement of fact.

'Well?'

'You went to see him,' he said baldly.

There were all kinds of answer to that, not least the truthful one. But I was so mad that he dared to *think* I was deceiving him, after yesterday . . . that he could imagine I was that kind of person, that I simply turned my head and refused to speak. I heard him go. I didn't turn round again for several minutes, and then I very busily and very angrily tidied up the room and got myself ready to go to the pub. Thank God I had to work, or I'd have been in floods of tears when Judy came back. As it was I could feel them inside, making a heavy ache in my throat.

I was about to go when Judy panted in.

'Sorry, I meant to come back sooner just in case . . . '

'In case what?' I said brightly. 'See you later.' I picked up my bag and went to the door.

'Are you okay?' she said.

'Of course I'm not okay,' I said in a hard voice. 'Perhaps you'll keep my secrets in future, and not go gossiping to Sam.'

'About what?' she said in real astonishment. I could have stayed and explained, but there wasn't time. I was obsessed with getting to work on time. As it was, I was quite early – which made my new boss seem quite pleased – and I spent the rest of the evening strenuously working at everything I was asked to do, chatting to customers whom I knew, being pleasant to the others, and all the time with this cold, hard thing inside me which wouldn't go away.

Jude was still awake when I got back after midnight.

'Had a good evening?' she said carefully.

'Yes, thanks,' I said distantly. I pulled my nightie from under my pillow and instead of just getting undressed in the middle of the room which I normally did I pulled the wardrobe door open and hid behind it.

'Sue?'

'What?' I growled ungraciously.

'If you could just tell me *what* I've done . . . '

'Oh . . . nothing, not really.' I shut the wardrobe door and looked at her. Only her face showed, over the quilt. 'It seems you told Sam I was going to Manchester and Sam told Paul and he got the wrong idea. That's all.'

'Oh . . . *bloody* men!' sighed Judy, and rolled onto her face. 'Honestly, Sue, why are they so damned possessive? Why *can't* . . . but there's no point wishing. I suppose I'd mind if Sam went out with lots of girls. Though it wasn't quite that, with me.'

'I suppose it was really a bit of my own fault,' I said gruffly, remembering our mumbled words last night. 'He asked if I'd written and I'd said yes. When of course I hadn't. Not to tell him what I said I'd told him.'

'Even so,' said Judy. 'No reason to get in such a state about it. Well, since we both seem to be single women again, what shall we do at the weekend?'

Good old Jude. I really needed her around to make me see sense. It didn't matter that much. I didn't know Paul that well. And if he was going to be a jealous type, then better I should know about it now.

I lay in bed and listed all the sensible things I should be thinking. But underneath, still, there was that lump of pain, telling me I was deceiving myself.

I was really glad to see my flat-mate when she got home from work on Friday. It had been a long day. I wasn't needed at the pub again till tomorrow, so it would be a long evening too. I wouldn't have said so to Judy, but I was meanly glad she'd had her bust-up with Sam so that we'd have an evening keeping each other company.

I had been tempted to ring Paul at work, then half-way to the phone box I'd thought I really mustn't, and walked back again. I did this about ten times before I thought it was really a bit stupid and that he wouldn't be able to speak to me let alone apologize or anything in front of other people and that it would only end up being depressingly embarrassing. And I'd probably end up doing the apologizing myself – remembering ruefully the days with Mike when I always said 'Sorry, it was my fault' even when it wasn't, just to keep the peace. And I was damned if I was going to apologize for anything I didn't think I'd done this time.

However, I had done something with my day.

'I've applied for college,' I told her, handing her a mug of tea. 'I didn't really think you were as serious as all that,' she said.

'Thanks. Just what I need,' taking a long drink of tea.

'I don't know whether I'm too late, but it's worth a try.'

'I've done something almost as daft,' she said shyly. 'Well, I haven't actually done anything yet, but I've written off to find out. I'm going to get a job abroad. And if I can't get a real one I shall go and do VSO work for a bit. I've always fancied seeing the world, and I might as well get someone to pay me for doing it.'

I sipped at the tea I'd almost forgotten. Suddenly there was hope in the future, not a bleak sameness, the threat of everything mapped out according to other people's plans, or just happening badly because I'd never stopped to think properly.

I stood up and rummaged in the bread bin. I was starved. There was marmite in the cupboard, and jam.

'Do you need this cheese for anything?' There was

about a four centimetre square of it.

'I *was* keeping it for a soufflé tonight and the other half of it for . . . '

'You don't. Good. Are we eating tonight?'

'*You* seem to be,' said Judy. 'I don't know whether there'll be anything left for me.'

'Or shall we blow some of our pot-money and go out to the Chinese or have a Tandoori? I've decided to give up domesticity for a day or two, till I get my self-respect back.'

I changed into my new two-piece, and while we were in the middle of discussing where we should go, there was a timid knock at the door. We looked at each other. I had a momentary, sinking, fear, and the hard knot in my stomach came back.

'Jehovah's Witnesses?' I suggested flippantly.

'About the only possibility,' agreed Judy.

'If we ignore them will they go away?'

'They know we're here,' said Judy despondently. 'There are blazing forty watt lights . . . '

'Remind me to get some more bulbs tomorrow so that we can see the charred bits on the chops,' I said.

' . . . and we've been talking at the tops of our voices for the last half hour.'

I went to the door.

It was almost like going back in time, except Judy wasn't putting on her make-up ready for a disco.

'Oh. Sam,' I said.

'Sorry. Mind if we come in?'

I stood aside for Sam and Paul to come into the room and fill it with their embarrassing presences.

'Sorry, Sam, I don't think I can come out tonight,'

said Judy distantly, becoming very busy at the sink.

'It's okay,' said Sam awkwardly. 'I just came to say I was sorry.'

Paul cleared his throat. 'And me,' he said.

Jude and I gazed at each other and I had to fight an insane desire to giggle.

'You've had to come together to hold hands?' said Judy, so bitingly that I was really sorry for both of them.

Sam opened his mouth and gulped a bit like a goldfish, but Paul tried to save things by saying, 'I just happened to meet him as he walked through the gate. I was coming to ask Sue if she'd like to come out for a meal. If you haven't already eaten, of course. Unless,' he added, tripping over his words a bit as if he knew he'd been talking too much to cover up their discomfiture, 'you'd rather not, of course.'

'Thanks, Paul. Only Jude and I were just going out. Perhaps another time.'

'Don't be silly, Sue. You know you'd like to,' came Judy's clear voice. 'We were going to go out together and have a meal and moan about you lot. But we can just as easily do that another day, like tomorrow.'

'No, we can't,' I said. 'I'll be working tomorrow. Thanks for asking, Paul, but Jude and I would really . . . '

'Tell you what,' said Judy. 'Suppose I make this idiot here take *me* out for a meal to make up for being bloody-minded earlier on, then we can all go out, which means that you and I, Sue, don't have to pay at all.'

Paul's broad grin showed that as far as he was concerned it was an ideal arrangement, and I had to giggle at Sam's face.

'Hang on, though,' I said. 'Er – Paul – do you mind if I have a private word first?' I did want to make it quite clear that I couldn't cope with jealousy, and if we were going to go on going out together, I wanted him to know now.

'If madam wouldn't mind accompanying me to the hostelry down the road,' he said, raising an eyebrow. I laughed, and went through the door he held open for me.

'Meet you in the Mitre in about half an hour, Jude?' I said.

'Right,' said Judy absently, her eyes only on Sam's face.

'That was tactful of you,' said Paul. 'Hope they make it up.'

'Of course they will,' I said. 'She was just annoyed at being bossed around.'

'Which is presumably what you want to talk about,' he said.

My jacket clung snugly at my throat, hung easily from my shoulders, warmed me in the cold of the evening. Or was it Paul's arm that was warming me?

'It was my fault,' I said, throwing caution and the future to the winds. 'Honestly, Paul, I'm sorry. It wasn't entirely untrue, either. When you asked me, I had made up my mind to write to him, but when he wrote and said come and visit, I thought I'd go and really make sure.'

'And did you make sure?'

I laughed, weakly, my face against his jacket. Its

roughness reassured me, somehow. 'Oh, Paul! Do you need to ask?'

'Not really,' he said softly. 'That was why I came back, why I knew I'd been stupid. I knew you couldn't be still in love with him if you meant what you said to me. It was the possibility that you might not have meant it that hurt.'

'You are daft!' I said. We were nearly at the pub. Suddenly I didn't want to go in there and have to make conversation with other people, have the bar staff see me with Paul and make comments about him when I went to work next day. I felt shy and ridiculously young and inexperienced, as if he was the first boy-friend I'd ever had. Tomorrow, perhaps, I'd feel diffe-rently, but now, when I'd so nearly lost the nicest guy I'd ever been out with . . .

'Would you mind if we didn't have a drink?' he murmured, slowing his step before we reached the door.

The only guy who'd ever thought the way I did as well as the nicest . .

'I don't mind at all,' I said, 'but Sam and Jude . . .'

'We could come back in half an hour, in case they've come to meet us . . .'

I laughed, and squeezed the hand which held mine. We walked away from the bright windows, and the moon was just rising behind the trees.

Ann Ruffel
Baby Face £1.25

Ros was fed up. Being small and baby-faced made her look years younger than seventeen – and it put the boys off. She longed to be tall and willowy like her best friend Marie.

When she met Mark, everthing changed – until Marie stole him away. This crushing blow made Ros decide to change her image. Baby Face was going to turn into a Mature Woman . . .

Friends for Keeps £1.25

Clive was twenty, sophisticated, fantastic looking, and different from anyone Frankie had ever known. But when he asked her out, Frankie knew she could never take him home to meet her mother. Not and subject him to one of those embarrassing family discussions that could range from politics to the pill. At first he treated her reluctance to take him home with amusement, but when he started to suspect that she was two-timing him, she had to explain a lot more than she'd bargained for – like her relationship with Alan.

Mary Hooper
Follow that Dream £1.25

Her parents' dream of moving to Cornwall is a nightmare blow for
Sally. How could she bear to leave London and be stuck away in the
country . . . with no mates, no music, no decent clothes, no parties
and no Ben, just when she was getting somewhere with him? But the
long-awaited visit from her best friend, Joanne, brings some
unexpected conflicts and Sally finds her determination to remain
apart slowly undermined by the presence of a boy called Danny . . .

Happy Ever After £1.25

Marcy is a romantic and when her sister, Sooty, announces her
engagement the wedding becomes the most important thing in her
life. Her own fantasies centre on Mick, the good-looking boy who
works next door to her, and, when they meet and like each other, she
longs for it to be 'forever and a day'. But real life has many
unexpected twists of plot and when the dreamed-of moment comes,
Marcy makes a surprising decision . . .

Pam Lyons
Danny's Girl £1.25

For sixteen-year-old Wendy, life was pretty straightforward. She
enjoyed her tomboy existence with her parents and brother Mike on
their farm in Norfolk. Then, late one sunny September afternoon,
Danny wandered into her life and suddenly Wendy's happy and
uncomplicated world is turned unside-down. Unsure of how she
should behave or what is expected of her, she allows herself to be
carried along in Danny's wake, and when he finds himself in trouble
at his exclusive boarding school she is his only ally. Eventually,
Wendy's fierce loyalty to the boy she loves leads them both deeper
and deeper into trouble . . .

All these books are available at your local bookshop or newsagent, or can be ordered direct from the publisher. Indicate the number of copies required and fill in the form below.

Send to: **CS Department, Pan Books Ltd., P.O. Box 40, Basingstoke, Hants. RG21 2YT.**

or phone: 0256 469551 (Ansaphone), quoting title, author and Credit Card number.

Please enclose a remittance* to the value of the cover price plus: 60p for the first book plus 30p per copy for each additional book ordered to a maximum charge of £2.40 to cover postage and packing.

*Payment may be made in sterling by UK personal cheque, postal order, sterling draft or international money order, made payable to Pan Books Ltd.

Alternatively by Barclaycard/Access:

Card No.

Signature:

Applicable only in the UK and Republic of Ireland.

While every effort is made to keep prices low, it is sometimes necessary to increase prices at short notice. Pan Books reserve the right to show on covers and charge new retail prices which may differ from those advertised in the text or elsewhere.

NAME AND ADDRESS IN BLOCK LETTERS PLEASE:

....

Name ——————————————————————————————

Address ——————————————————————————————

——————————————————————————————

——————————————————————————————

——————————————————————————————

3/87